The Greatest Test of Courage by Ronda Hassig follows the fate of American POWs beginning with the 1942 surrender to the Japanese in the Philippines. The story of Eddie Mack and his comrades is harrowing, vivid, and takes readers to the primal existence of living under the torment of the Japanese. Moment by moment, readers will be captivated by the intense circumstances Eddie must experience. His character is admirable as he portrays a faithful and positive hero in the hell of war. The story transcends readers to the vulgar conditions our American heroes had to endure for years, while highlighting the resilience of the human spirit. The story is captivating and unveils the true courage among American warriors in the shadows of history.

— *Kristi Yeager, Library Media Specialist*

The book is a work of historical fiction that was beautifully written. It is very heavy because of how brutal the Japanese were. I liked how it told what really happened, and not a lot a bunch of lies to soften it. It was fascinating and eye opening, and it taught me a lot. What I also liked was how the facts weren't written in some sort of clumsy way, the author incorporated it into the story. I would recommend this book although I would caution certain age groups because, like I said, some parts are very graphic and bloody.

— *Taylor Sloan, 8th grade student, Overland Park, Kansas*

Strong read! A clean, clear story of heroism in the face of massive opposition. Eddie's ups and downs were absorbing and drew me in. The story did a nice job of pulling non-fiction into a story that kept the reader engaged. The follow up at the end, the notes on sources, and the extras such as that added a nice teachable moment to the material.

— *Jeff Benes, Secondary Teacher and Iraq Veteran*

D1600690

THE
GREATEST
TEST OF
COURAGE

[signature]

To my long time
friend and fellow
West Pointer

[signature]

THE
GREATEST
TEST OF
COURAGE

RONDA HASSIG

DEEDS PUBLISHING | ATLANTA

Published by Deeds Publishing in Athens, GA
www.deedspublishing.com

Printed in The United States of America

Cover design by Mark Babcock

Library of Congress Cataloging-in-Publications data is available upon request.

ISBN 978-1-947309-24-1

Books are available in quantity for promotional or premium use. For information, email info@deedspublishing.com.

First Edition, 2018

10 9 8 7 6 5 4 3 2 1

"The greatest test of courage on the earth is to bear defeat without losing heart."

—*Robert G. Ingersoll*

"History without tragedy does not exist…"

—*H. G. Adler*

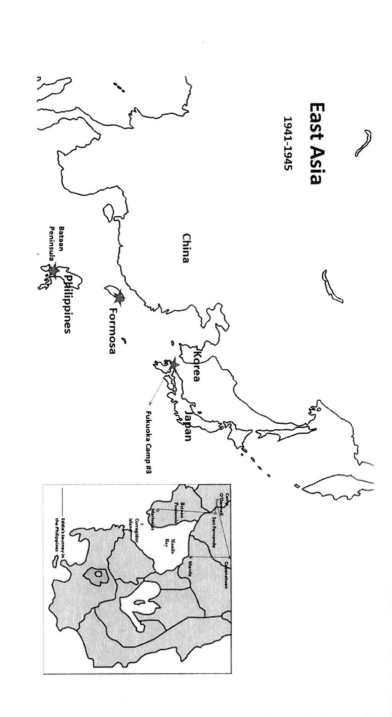

East Asia

1941-1945

China

Batan Peninsula

Philippines

Formosa

Korea

Japan

Fukuoka Camp #3

Camp O'Donnell

Bataan Peninsula

Manila

Corregidor Island

San Fernando

Manila Bay

Cabanatuan

Manila

Eddie's Journey in the Philippines

Using Slang in War

This book includes language that civilized human beings would not use today. However, historians and authors must make the decision to use the language of the time or risk rewriting history. Slang terms like "Japs," "Nips," "Slant-eyed ants" or "SEAS," or "Krauts" are offensive and deplorable, but served a very important role in World War II. It wasn't just soldiers that used this offensive language but also the media and elected officials. If you can use slang to describe your enemy, you can eliminate their humanity. When you do that your enemy is easier to kill.

Edward Clement Mack, West Point Class of 1925

Prologue

This book is true, but it is written as a work of historical fiction. The people and events are real, but some of their thoughts and conversations are not. Lt. Col. Edward Clement Mack (Eddie) was a Japanese prisoner of war in the Philippines. He wrote numerous letters prior to the war, four letters after the Japanese invasion of Bataan, and eight POW correspondence cards during his imprisonment. These primary sources survive and were used as sources while writing this book. Other sources used were letters written to Nancy, after the war, by Eddie's fellow prisoners and underground contacts.

This is the story of one man's experience. In reality, it is also a testament to tens of thousands of American soldiers that lived and died at the hands of the Japanese in World War II.

When in doubt as to what Eddie might have experienced, I relied on other prisoner's diaries and memoirs, as well as secondary sources.

All sources have bias, but when you triangulate, you

are hopefully able to find the truth. I did not have the privilege of knowing Eddie, but I have no doubt that his story deserves to be told. His son is my husband's cousin and, until her death, we spent every 4th of July in Leavenworth, Kansas with his mother Nancy. I remember all her stories about Eddie and his Silver Star and three Bronze Stars. I found out about the discovery of Eddie's West Point ring when John let the family know it had been returned to him. It was then that I knew I had to write this book.

Finally, I am a middle school librarian, historian, and author. When I first began writing this book, it was for my 8th grade students and other young adult readers. There is very little written for young audiences about the Bataan Death March or the Japanese treatment of enemy soldiers. I hope this book may help fill this niche.

Most importantly, I hope that whoever reads this book, young or old, will learn about courage, empathy, and perseverance. They will know that these virtues take great strength and effort, and sometimes you are not rewarded for your efforts in this world. With faith, the true rewards come in the next.

I

In the military history of the United States, this had never happened. Well, in 1865 maybe, but that was on American soil and involved two Americas, so that didn't count. We would be the first. These were actual thoughts running through his brain even as he watched men of all shapes and sizes stumble out of the jungle, their ribs sticking out of their bare chests as they waved their gray undershirts in the dense air that surrounded them. The cacophony of insects, frogs, and monkeys—the constant sound of the forest—stopped abruptly in the gravity of the moment.

The endless stream of men with downcast tear-stained faces, some quiet, some coughing due to illness, continued, never ending. Men staggered. A few were dragging brothers behind them, limp and heavy. Unarmed and defenseless, they were at the mercy of their captors. Fear hung in the air and stunk like death.

Surrender. Capitulation. Done.

2

If we were going to do it, let us do it together. Yes, we were embarrassed and we all felt yellow and ashamed. But it was yield or die, and this was our only alternative. 24,000 men were sick the day before surrender. No use fighting any more. Too sick and too tired to carry on. Maybe we were even saving lives by surrendering? We were saving ours for sure. Hell, we'd given the army at least four months to regroup after Pearl Harbor. The Japanese had lost 20,000 men in the 100-day siege of the Philippines. Hadn't we done enough?

Why did we have to walk for heaven's sake? In his present state, lots of things didn't make a lot of sense to Eddie. Why couldn't the Japanese just dump us in trucks and move us to wherever the hell they had in mind?

Eddie had details and logistics filed in his brain like the stacks in a library. He just had to mind-walk through his narrow aisles and locate his source. When it finally dawned on him, it hadn't been complicated at all. It was only a few days ago that General King had given the secret signal "Crash!" Surrender was imminent and it was time to destroy everything. God forbid that any of the antique equipment get into the hands of the advancing Japs. Old or not, if the tanks, trucks, ammunition, hand grenades, communication gear, even c-rations, could be scavenged, it would be aiding the Japanese. This was unthinkable. They would later regret the loss of the c-rations, but he remembered the men's weird elation at being able to gear down and drive over the tins of tasteless spaghetti and aged peaches. Maybe we should have left the tins of God-awful reprocessed meat for the Nips. It was wild really. When the men were told that every item important to the war effort had to be demolished, they took the destruction to the next level. Did our GI's pour sand and dirt into their trucks to disable them? NO. They shot armor-piercing shells into their engines! Tanks were drained of their oil and then driven as fast as they would go until the engines froze up. Men gambled their precious cigarettes on which tanks would run the furthest.

He hadn't witnessed the craziest demolition, but he'd heard about it for days. There was a tunnel entrance in the bay area used for the massive storage of gasoline containers. The Japanese needed fuel as badly as the Americans did, so this dump had to go. It was decided that it would be easiest to just blow it up. Obviously, the decision was made much too quickly, without regard for safety or the real-time consequences. Of course, no one had ever practiced this drill before. The fire bomb, as in the eruption of Krakatoa, was so enormous that it spewed rock missiles into the harbor, killing four unsuspecting sailors a half mile away.

Now it dawned on him—this was why the prisoners were being forced to walk. There were no trucks to carry so many men. We had effectively gutted them. Any trucks the Japanese possessed to carry their soldiers to Corregidor were ones they had landed at Bataan months ago. The hulks of the American trucks were pure shrapnel now, rusting in the jungle heat and humidity.

He also knew where they were going. This road led to Camp O'Donnell, the area used to train Filipino soldiers before the war started. Unfinished, it contained at least the necessary foundations for holding our soldiers.

3

The Japanese were dumbstruck at first, but that quickly changed when they realized the enormity of their task—so many prisoners you couldn't see the end of the lines down the rugged but dead-straight jungle road. One look at these prisoners and one quickly realized that they were in bad shape. Hunger, disease, and heat had drained their energy, both physically and mentally. Many struggled to stand erect. Yet the Japanese paid no notice. What they saw were men that had killed their buddies a few days ago in some last-ditch skirmish, and regardless of the men's pitiful condition, it meant absolutely nothing to the guards. Their captives had lost face in their surrender. Had they had Japanese courage, they would have never surrendered—fought to the last man or committed hara-kiri in the Samurai warrior's tradition. Each Japanese was encultured in those traditional mores.

Eddie stood on the road, rigid and defiant. His release from the hospital only a few weeks earlier gave him an advantage over many of his fellow soldiers. He'd been recuperating from an almost-fatal shrapnel wound to the stomach, and those three months had given him time to rest and regain some of his strength before going back on duty. Still, his brain refused to register what his eyes were seeing as the men began to snake forward.

The Japanese wanted everyone on the road, if you could call it that. So much movement of heavy equipment made it seem more like a rutted cow path back in Nanticoke. The dust was some four to six inches deep. It got in your lungs and eyes and made you mad thirsty. Men hobbled side by side and initially tried to keep pace with each other. Eddie was on the inside of a row when he learned a lifesaving lesson. If you could find a position inside a row and not walk on the ends you were safer. As the prisoners slowly progressed along the road, they had to share space with Japanese military equipment, including tanks and trucks carrying troops. Intermittently, a Japanese soldier would have "their fun" and abuse the prisoners with their swords or guns.

They had walked only a short distance when Eddie's mate got nailed with a random blow to the head from a Japanese soldier hanging out the back of his truck. The force of the blow knocked the entire row sideways like dominoes. Eddie maintained his balance as if shedding a block on the West Point gridiron, but the two men further inside crumpled to the ground. The guilty Jap laughed maniacally. The sound echoed in Eddie's ears as the bastard in the truck bumped on down the road, away from the wounded and dazed men. The stricken prisoner lay almost motionless in the carabao (Philippine water buffalo, the local mode of transportation for the majority of the Philippine population) dung he'd been trudging through. The blood from his wound began pooling, coagulating with the dust. He was still breathing, but it was erratic. With the help of several other prisoners, Eddie was able to move him off the road.

One of the guards noticed the commotion and sprinted over to keep everyone moving. When he found them trying to revive the wounded man, he became angry and began screaming. His language was indecipherable, but his intent was obvious and threatening. MOVE! QUICKLY! NOW! The injured man was barely alive, but Eddie tried to get him to stand. The guard screamed again and waved his pistol at Eddie and his unconscious comrade. Eddie's confusion was evident. He kept his hold on the limp man. The closeness of the shot paralyzed Eddie. The guard's aim was deadly. When he pointed the gun at Eddie's now debris-splattered face, he knew it was time to move.

The dead soldier fell away. Helping a dead man was futile. Eddie knew that the death meant nothing more to the guard than the unconscious swat to drive away a gnat, and momentarily he might join the corpse in the dust. Eddie's body felt so heavy that it was hard to pull one leg in front of the other. But he turned deliberately and ploddingly rejoined the others.

4

If this had been the only incident, the mental scars might have been somewhat repairable. But the routine played out over and over again as the guards became frustrated with the starving, diseased, and exhausted men. And there were so many of them. When General King had surrendered on April 9, the Japanese high command was expecting maybe 20,000 to 30,000 prisoners of war, but they now controlled some 50,000 more. They weren't the Japanese' priority here; Corregidor was. Any manpower that had to be used to control and move prisoners was wasted. The focus was the fortress on Manila Bay.

For the last four months, Bataan had been on half rations. Most of the command weren't even getting 1,000 calories a day, barely enough to sustain life lying down, let alone moving without food or water.

Water was the most important commodity to all the prisoners, but it soon became apparent that the guards had no intention of letting anyone have even a sip. There was water everywhere on Bataan, literally coming out of the ground, and it was clean, drinkable water. Most of the guards wouldn't let the prisoners anywhere near it. As the minutes, hours, and days stretched endlessly before the soldiers, many became desperate. This desperation fueled the sadism of the guards, and events spiraled quickly out of control. The Japs didn't play nice either.

Most of the Japanese carried a sword they had purchased once they joined the army. As tradition dictated, they were well-practiced swordsmen and took every opportunity to practice their skills on anyone that angered them, couldn't understand them, or just didn't move fast enough to please them. Or perhaps it was just random. Those swords were regularly used to run men through with a quick thrust or to decapitate. Torsos and heads littered the march as a grim foreboding of each man's implicit fate. After a while, the Americans became numb to death, only concerned with their own survival. Of course, their hatred for the Asiatic barbarians was exploding within them. The Japs seemed not to notice, nor care.

5

There is no doubt that war brings out the most deplorable behavior in human beings. One has to look no further than the Nazis and the gruesome deaths of millions in "the camps," or the Red Army and its massacre and rape of women and children at the end of World War II. But the Japanese military culture had a special propensity for instilling fear and terror in the minds and psyches of their enemy. The philosophy of "Bushido" or the "Way of the Warrior" had been practiced in Japan since the 12th century. Throughout the Code's long history, it was infused with the beliefs of Zen, Buddhism, and Confucianism. In Confucianism, the Samurai was to be a "perfect gentleman" to everyone, but most importantly to those weak or poor. Sadly, the tenets of kindness and honesty were sorely missing in Bataan. Rather, personal honor and loyalty to the emperor were most highly regarded. This obligation to one's "Human God" was supreme, no matter the cost.

Bushido wasn't just a way of life for the Japanese warrior class. At the time of World War II, it was ethically practiced by everyone in Japan. The core values included having a "martial spirit," loyalty, and family values. It was practiced by everyone, including the smallest child. The war at home demanded courage and self-discipline once the bombs began to drop and food became scarce. But the most dangerous value of Bushido was honor. Honor was so key to the Samurai code that in order to insure its eternal existence, one could never surrender and must, if necessary, commit suicide to keep dishonor from occurring. If one wanted to die properly, he invoked "Seppuku," a ritual self-disembowelment, often accompanied by simultaneous decapitation by an honored comrade.

Bushido is no excuse for how the Japanese treated the American or Filipino soldiers on Bataan, but it does explain some of their actions toward those captured. Surrender caused the death of hundreds, if not thousands, of men. In the code of Bushido, there really wasn't anything worse than surrender. Surrender meant dishonoring one's self, one's family, Japan, and the Emperor. This belief was so contrary to American thought. Surrender wasn't desirable, but capture was better than death. It was what the West believed, a religious view that continues today. Life is precious.

Western armies also believed the Japanese would be honorable in how they treated us while in captivity, on marches, and in their POW camps. Maybe belief is not the right word—hoped. Everyone was aware of what had happened in the Rape of Nanking, but with the declaration of war and the Geneva Convention, it was anticipated that Western prisoners would be treated with respect, rather than the vile contempt reserved for Asian enemies. But, this was not to be. If anything, the Code of Bushido brought out the animalistic behaviors of bygone days.

Additionally, the men left to guard the prisoners on the march to Camp O'Donnell and Camp Cabanatuan were the dregs of the Japanese military. The better soldiers were ahead, preparing for the invasion of Corregidor. The guards for the POWs were typically the newest recruits and, as such, had been abused and ridiculed by their commanding officers and other more seasoned men stationed along with them. These were hardly the Japanese' best and brightest. In reality, guarding men who had admitted defeat, was as shameful as being the actual okubyōmono.

Finally, many American soldiers felt the guards were humiliated about their body size and height in comparison to the American troops. Often some of the worst treatment doled out by the Japanese was toward the largest and most fit men.

6

Eddie saw the Japanese need for domination first hand. On the third day of the march, an American soldier of large stature was walking several rows in front of Eddie—large stature as in six foot, four inches tall, and even on half rations he out-weighed most of the Japanese by fifty pounds. Quite suddenly he staggered forward several yards, almost like he'd tripped. He dropped to his knees, rolling over on his back. He struggled to sit up, and when he did, Eddie got a good look at him. The rags that were his actual clothing were drenched in sweat. His face was flushed, his eyes wild, and Eddie figured he was suffering from a bout of malaria. Regardless of his complications, he was blocking the line, the path for the other prisoners. When he was unable to move out of the way, a Japanese soldier pulled his sword from his belt and ran him through with a two-handed thrust.

A hideous sound. Quick. The dying man drew a deep breath as the blade plunged in and exhaled slowly as the blade slid out, and he crumpled onto himself. Death on the road.

Tanks rumbled down the road and not one slowed to go around. Soldiers riding on the top of tanks watched with rifles at the ready. Each saw the body; none warned the driver to swerve. Nine tanks ran over the corpse. When the last one rolled on, only a dark shadow remained on the road where once there had been a man — a man loved by his mother, wife, children; a man whose only crime was being too ill to move quickly. Bits of cloth and button fragments intermingled with crushed bones were the only signs that a living being had once lain on this spot.

Eddie turned his head quickly when he saw the first tank and heaved into the dust. Little water and no food meant his stomach was empty, but dry or not, his stomach revolted at the scene in front of it. The prisoners walking behind him, say twenty rows back, would never even know they had lost a fellow prisoner.

There were many horrific incidents along the road that day, but one of the worst Eddie would mercifully not have to witness. No one knows what precipitated the Jap's rage or hatred. But when it was all over, 400 Filipino soldiers were not only dead but no longer recognizable as men. Loud screaming and cursing by the Japanese soldiers set off a swinging of swords as the guards surrounded the dazed soldiers of the 91st Philippine Division.

There were even rumors later that telephone wire was used and men were beheaded. The hacking and slashing only ceased when all were lying in pieces by the roadside and the guards were exhausted. Many were deranged during the slaughter as adrenalin coursed through their veins.

For the victims, both dead and watching, there had been little food or water in 72 hours or longer. Many were struggling to put one foot in front of the other and it was no secret that the treatment of the Philippine soldier was even crueler than that of the American. No man was a match for the deranged swordsmen. Their only defense once the melee began was to cover their faces with their arms. When the slaughter was finished, the sweating, panting Japanese guards cleaned their gory swords on a pant leg, sheathed their weapons, and shoved the stunned bystanders forward down the road. Once more the sounds of the jungle were shocked into silence. No frogs, no monkeys, no birds. Quiet. Still. Dante's Inferno.

7

Eddie witnessed atrocities that defied belief. For the last four months, he had seen death. Carnage was a given, a part of war. But what transpired on the way to Camp O'Donnell would later be called the Bataan Death March. And with very good reason.

Death was on the 65-mile road. It was in the jungle that strangled the very air the men breathed. It was in the sun that scorched exposed bare skin and dehydrated a body within a few hours; at the artesian springs that drew men like moths to a fire, only to feel the sting of fine Japanese steel. It was in the wind that carried the whimpering cries of 18-year-old boys who had just left their mothers six months ago. It was in the stench that was the decomposing bodies and men suffering from dysentery, diarrhea running down their legs.

No matter how badly the Japanese treated the prisoners though, the Filipino people did their best to thwart their shared enemy. Eddie saw them standing by the roads at different intervals on the journey. Most were women, and the pity they wore on their faces was palpable. As the prisoners stumbled by, civilians standing roadside would hand them a cup of water, a morsel to eat. The men were always appreciative. The kindnesses were soon found out and the Japanese would stab the locals in the stomach or simply shoot them. No matter how hungry or thirsty Eddie became, he vowed he would accept nothing from these kind people. He did not want their deaths setting up permanent residence in his already-cluttered conscience.

Sometimes Eddie would close his eyes so tight he thought his head would explode. Anything to make the scenes disappear. No matter — the same horrifying images returned again and again. They replayed at every stop, over and over, no matter how much he prayed for rest to come. All the men were suffering from the same horrors. Everyone dealt with the mental agony in their own way.

Eddie was a devout Catholic. He wore his faith like an invisible shield, and he carried his rosary like a secret weapon. In his shirt pocket, he hid his most powerful talisman — a picture of his son Johnny. Not everyone was so fortunate. If you lacked the ability to block out the terrors you were seeing and focus on memories of loved ones back home, you were doomed. Some men became so despondent they were unable to move. Stopping meant certain death. You stopped when the Japanese wanted you to. Corpses filled the ditches as proof.

As Eddie put one foot in front of the other, his eyes on the primitive road, he reminisced about swimming with his wife and son only a summer ago. The cool water soothed his weary body. He could still feel Johnny on his hip as he walked him round and round, the boy running his hand through the water, giggling when it tickled his tiny fingers.

His right hand went instinctively to his front pocket where he secreted his treasured rosary. Given to him by his favorite sister, Helen, the beads could be counted one at a time, each one assuring him peace, slowing the cadence of his heart. Thank God for memories. Some would inspire and sustain him in the coming months and years. Others would haunt and remind him to be cautious and always wary.

8

There were specific objects on the walk that meant instant abuse or death. If you were carrying any of these in your pockets or on your body, you needed to hide them or dispose of them before the guards saw or caught you with them. Anything of value, like a watch or ring, was free for the taking. Put up a fight and you risked the chance of losing more than your jewelry. You could be walking in line one minute and stopped and frisked by a guard the next. What in the hell was he looking for? Nobody had a weapon, for God's sake. It was your watch they wanted. It was your ring. One prisoner was wearing his West Point ring when a guard grunted for him to remove it. When he didn't move fast enough, the guard swiftly pulled his sword and chopped off the prisoner's hand at the wrist. When the hand dropped to the dusty road, the guard reached down nonchalantly and removed the ring. He grinned at the prisoner as he stuffed the ring in his pocket and walked away, wiping his sword across another prisoner's buttocks before it was re-sheathed.

Blood spewed everywhere as the men nearby tried to stop the frothy red spray by applying a filthy tourniquet made from the tatters of someone's shirt.

To be caught with money was almost always lethal. Not American or Philippine money, but Japanese money. Never mind that you had been given it as change for goods so having it on your person was completely innocent and benign. If you had Japanese cash in your pockets, you had obviously taken it off a dead Japanese soldier. True or not, the guards believed this, and out came the swords once again. This time men lost their heads. If the guard was strong enough, the beheading was quick and on the spot. If the guard was smaller and less muscled, he would demand the prisoner drop to his knees and stare at the ground in front of him. Execution of another soldier, a brother, was a sight no American or Filipino was accustomed to. The only response for most men was shock.

Hunger and thirst had made most zombies. Watching a head tumble into the ditch was just one more surreal scene for each soldier to lock in his memory vault. If you had seen it happen and didn't get rid of all your cash, you were a fool and not paying attention. There would be relentless searches. Guards changed duty every few hours, and the new ones would be looking for trophies as well.

Eddie watched all and learned quickly that his own West Point ring brought danger. For the time being, it would be safe down the front of his underwear, tucked into the elastic band around his waist, but soon he would have to find a more comfortable and less obvious spot. Thinking about it would consume his thoughts for a while and allow him to focus on something other than the butchery taking place all around him. The scene constantly playing out before his eyes was reminiscent of slaughter houses of the great Mid-western cities, Chicago and Kansas City, the land of his Nancy.

For all the bloodshed, most men became consumed with one thing and one thing only—THIRST. Water, water everywhere, but not a drop to be had. Eddie began to think that the guards were hoping the prisoners would all die so they could join their fellow warriors at Corregidor. Men became so thirsty they were willing to die for a drop of liquid. A muddy puddle, a diluted pool of carabao urine—it made no difference to the dying men.

And it wasn't just water but exhaustion and sickness that plagued the men for some 65 miles over almost two weeks. By the time Eddie reached Camp O'Donnell, he along with all the prisoners, was starving, exhausted, and dehydrated. Everyone had either malaria, dysentery, pneumonia, beriberi, diphtheria, or a combination thereof. Some one thousand Americans and upwards of 15,000 Filipinos died on the march. Although Eddie had seen only a fraction of these deaths, the trauma, both mentally and physically, had only just begun. He was also mindful enough to recognize many Japs were pretty scrawny themselves. Their bellies were empty, too. If the Japanese army was expecting guards to forage for protein to go with their meager supply of rice it was difficult to do when you were doing sentry duty. Eddie's sympathies for the guards was non-existent, but the reality was there just wasn't enough food for tens of thousands of men, no matter which side they were on.

Throughout the march, men normally died by themselves or with another man. Someone would finally reach the breaking point and run for water. When another brother ran to help, they both died. For some of the prisoners, death was a relief.

9

Finally, the march ended. They had reached San Fernando. Their agony was over. Rail cars were waiting. Their numb and weary legs would have a respite. But the cars weren't made for humans, and certainly not 80 to 100 of them. The men were crammed in so tightly that some suffocated. When the first men on began to complain that there were too many riders, the men still getting on weren't allowed to wait—not with a sword poking you in the back. For three to four tormented hours they waited for the train to move. When it finally pushed off, they had a two to five-hour trip to Capas in front of them; an eternity. The dead wished they had kept walking.

Eddie was lucky enough to have been last on. Unfortunately, he realized this too late after he had pushed forward to the middle of the car, there to remain the entire trip. Yet his misfortune gave some other poor chap on the perimeter a chance at fresh air. Yes, those last on got to sit near the open boxcar door and feel the hot breeze on their worn bodies. Eddie knew there were others in worse shape. Those first on were not only smashed against the wooden frame, but their exposed skin burned at the touch of the super-heated metal. The boxcar had basked in the intense midday sun, cooking the rivets and hinges while leaving the interior depleted of breathable air. Almost everyone had soiled themselves along the walk. The Japanese allowed no one a break to relieve themselves. They halted when it was time for a guard change and that happened every two to three hours. Dysentery didn't wait for breaks, so on the walk, and in the trains, the stench was overpowering. There was no judging by any man. Every prisoner had surely suffered this indignity.

Eddie rode standing as did all the men around him. Bodies endured crippling cramps and tedious twitching until the ride was over. The car was filled with constant moans. Each held his neighbors up and literally every sense was pounded with spirit-draining stimuli. The hot, sticky bodies literally wore each other. They wreaked. Most men gagged and retched in this oppressive sewer. This only compounded the misery—a vicious circle. Men's hollowed cheeks and tear-stained faces loomed large. The constant sounds of despair pervaded this miserable cage. There was no escaping it, so Eddie tried to put his mind in another place.

10

Eddie's mind drifted back to the history of how he got to this miserable place. The summer of 1900 saw the second modern Olympics, the first ever outside of Greece, as well as the World's Fair, both in Paris. One of the most astonishing achievements and the centerpiece at the Exposition was a refractor, the largest telescope ever built. With two glass lenses over three feet wide and 186 feet long, the tube that held them was almost 200 feet long! Sadly, the beast was so enormous that it was unable to move or take aim at heavenly objects. Had that refractor been able to focus across the Atlantic and into tiny Nanticoke, Pennsylvania on June 15th, it would have seen the birth of a future American hero, christened nine days later as Edward Clement Mack. Very little is known about Edward's childhood because all who knew him have passed and there was mostly only an oral record. He was one of seven children born to Joseph and Victoria Mack.

Undoubtedly he was bright, robust, and devoutly

Catholic. Each of these traits would play a critical role in the man he would eventually become. His toughness became best defined when, early in high school, he distinguished himself at a local carnival. A wrestler, Joe Mott, challenged all comers to a bout on the hard dirt and grass on that venue. A young Edward Mack accepted his dare and defeated him in a quick but hard-fought battle.

After high school, Edward joined the Pennsylvania National Guard, and his high scoring entrance exam later got him accepted into the prestigious United States Military Academy at West Point. He would go on to prove his strength and prowess representing the Academy on the gridiron for three years and in the boxing, ring where he was heavyweight champion. No matter what he did in the military or in life, he always gave 150 percent. He had the physical and mental tenacity of a bulldog.

But there was a uniqueness to his dogged purpose, and it was this that drove his fellow classmates crazy. He loved to sing in the morning! Between reveille and breakfast, he would burst out in obbligatos and folk songs. There was nothing more irritating at 5:00am to his fellow cadets than hearing, "By the Light of the Silvery Moon" while trying to wake up. Yet everyone loved Eddie, regardless of his propensity to be a morning person.

His intelligence was a natural gift, but that didn't mean he sat on his laurels. In his senior year, he showed how devoted he was to his studies, whether in class or on break, when he should have gone home to be with family. He took the peace and quiet time to pore through law volumes. His work ethic was daunting and admired by his peers and teachers…

Eddie was jerked back to reality when the man leaning against him became dead weight; literally. He swayed with the rhythm of the train's movement but he had to brace his stance and lock his knees to keep from falling. His neighbor was no longer living. It had all been too much for him. How many others on the train had met their limits? How much longer would they have to hold on?

What was that irritating pain at his middle? It wasn't that it hurt him really but it kept annoying him. He moved his hand down to check the exact spot. Of course, it was his ring that he'd hidden in the elastic around his waist. It was almost as if the ring was trying to get his attention. He slipped his right ring finger into its warm grip. He put his hand up close to his heart and slipped into a tormented sleep.

He dreamed about being a "firstie." Full of pride and enthusiasm, he was finally going into his senior year. He was pretty proud of himself, too. The room where the ring ceremony took place was dark and candlelit. Everyone was in full military dress and dates had come from nearby colleges. It was a hushed and serious dinner with the presenting of rings, custom designed by a Tiffany Co. metalsmith, before the dancing. The artisan had taken great care to use the finest materials, since his work was going to be worn by a West Pointer, maybe even a hero.

All of his brothers called him Eddie. He was a warrior in the boxing ring and on the football field, fiercely fair and always, always, a rule follower. He was older than many of his peers. His time in the Pennsylvania Guard had prepared him for the rigors of West Point where he excelled every year, both academically and athletically. His chosen branch was the infantry. He was focused and anyone who knew him or worked with him was attached to him immediately.

After graduation in 1925, he served the army in

many places: Georgia, Alabama, and New York. Most notable was his stint in Panama where jungle life in heat and humidity would help him later in the Philippines. "Duty, Honor, Country" were immortalized across his face — the very words all West Pointers lived by.

His dream took him back to 1937. The year he fell in love because he'd finally met the perfect woman; Nancy. Man she was really swell. Tall, slim, younger, and dressed like she'd just stepped out of Vogue magazine — she was a real dish! She was her own woman. She was born and raised in Kansas City, Kansas and was the daughter of a doctor. She had attended a private college in Baltimore for a year but returned home to finish her degree at Kansas University. Wasting no time post-graduation, she headed to Dallas and SMU to get her master's degree. She loved English and literature and spent time with her professors and peers in England and Scotland so she could be close to the birthplaces of her literary champions.

Teaching was her chosen profession and she eventually ended up at a private girl's school on Staten Island in New York. It was there that Eddie met her. He was stationed nearby, and it was love at first sight. He was immediately smitten with her bold confidence, quick wit, and obvious intelligence. Eddie always felt like he'd gotten the better end of the deal when it came to their relationship, sealed on December 4, 1937 at Ft. Jay, Governor's Island in New York.

They really were the perfect couple, and just over a year later they were blessed with a son — John. Nancy almost didn't make it to the hospital when the Governor's Island ferry captain refused to leave until his scheduled departure! Frantic, Eddie forgot his winter coat but made it to the hospital in time for the delivery and to welcome their first child. He reminded Nancy of this special night a few years later and the memory of sitting in a chair in her hospital room. A light had shown out over the water of the harbor. In the morning, he realized that the light he'd watched all night was the Statue of Liberty. Life couldn't get any better, or so it seemed.

Fort McKinley in the Philippines was the family's first foreign station. They arrived in early 1940. Luzon was a little piece of paradise, America's most distant footprint in the Far East. The officer corps and their families resided in fine houses. They swam at the officer's club pool and partied on Friday and Saturday nights in the officer's club dining room and bar. During the football season, they were able to listen to the Army/Navy football game with all the other families and parade out mules and goats on the green lawn after a touchdown. Life was almost surreal, especially later when it all came tumbling down around them.

1 2

The train began to slow down and Eddie felt the dream's visions dissipate, but he willed the dream to stay. He was successful for the time being. He saw the newspaper headlines and remembered the Japanese incursion into Manchuria, in 1932, had heightened tensions. Japan's insatiable thirst for raw materials, sorely lacking on the home islands, continued south in a push through central China. Little by little, the world came to know of the brutality of the Japanese advance. Word leaked of mass decapitations, live human bayonet practice on civilians, unspeakable horrors perpetrated upon women, even genocide, first from Nanking and later through the whispers of survivors fleeing south. The scope and breadth of the Japanese war plan was still unknown to those U.S. soldiers stationed on Luzon, in Manila and in the fortress at Corregidor, as they went about their daily assignments.

He and Nancy, however, were both obsessed with newspapers. They read as many as they could get their hands on. Even so, the moments, hours, and days they spent with each other were for getting to know not only each other as man and wife but also as mother and father to their young and growing son. They only needed time; but time was running out.

In May of 1941, the clock stopped. Nancy and Johnny left Manila like the other officers' families. Loved ones had to go home in case of an attack that was sure to come, but no one wanted to think or talk about it. A marriage less than four years old and a tiny son still getting to know his father were put on hold. The child had an ominous and innate sensitivity for long goodbyes. If he'd only known. But maybe he did. Kisses and hugs were kept short so as to not upset the child. And Eddie's macho reassurances that this would be a quick farewell and an ultimate fast reunion didn't convince little Johnny. The final "take care of your Momma" between father and son was still ringing in the air as the ship pulled away from the Manila harbor. As it began its protracted journey east, Eddie stood stoic and watched the ship longingly until it was out of sight. He was thankful for his sunglasses. His heart was hurting. He already missed them. But first and foremost, he was an army officer from the Point, and duty always came before anything else, even love and loneliness. Leadership was needed, but how badly wouldn't become clear for another six months.

It was not until the 7th of December in 1941 that the scale and reality of the Japanese empire's expansionist quest became reality for MacArthur and his troops.

13

Eddie had put his nose to the grindstone and worked hard to keep his mind off his absent family. He socialized as always, playing golf, watching polo, or having cocktails at the Officers' Club. He met some amazing people, including the famous Clare Boothe Luce, playwright, war correspondent, and wife of the owner of LIFE and Time Magazine. He and the other officers were impressed with this true woman of the world. Eddie had even written Nancy about meeting her. Both women shared a spunk that Eddie admired, but Nancy was his one true love that even the immense distance couldn't change. He made sure Nancy understood this.

His letters home were written with great care to keep his dearests informed. He wrote almost every day, and he never neglected to tell Nancy about what daily life was like at work and when possible, at their old home. To Eddie, it was like sitting on the veranda and talking with her. He kept nothing from her and was honest, even if it might frighten her. He married her for her strength, and she was going to need it in the days, months, and years ahead. However, all of his letters home assured Nancy that the Japanese would not attack the Philippines. They had too many other problems to deal with, but primarily oil. The islands didn't have the fuel they needed so the Philippines could only offer them trouble. When he did waver on his assurances of the Philippines' safety, he would tell her so.

Eddie fretted about the changing of commanders from General Grunert to General MacArthur. Eddie was anxious about the army's lack of preparedness in the face of the looming Japanese menace. Attack or not, he wanted to be ready; that was what sixteen years of training had assured him would keep everyone safe.

MacArthur's plan to beef up the Philippine army separate from the American army would cost money, and Eddie didn't want Nancy or Johnny paying for this "fleecing" as he called it. Most importantly, Eddie was concerned about the Philippine army and its ability to defend themselves.

Speaking of the differences between the Philippine and American soldier, Eddie insisted that the Filipinos lacked training and confidence in their ability to fight. He felt that with American commanders, the Filipinos would make good soldiers. It would take time, and time was something they really didn't have much of. Rather than train the Filipinos separately, he wanted them to be integrated into the American units so U.S. soldiers could role model their martial skills and instill how to fight.

Eddie shook his head in disbelief when this story was told to him. His roommate, Jess, came home one day with what Eddie called a "revolting" story. The medical inspection officers were checking out the new toilets set up for the Philippine Army and found that soldiers were using the bushes as a bathroom and the toilets to wash their hands! Eddie scoffed that this was the well-trained Filipino army that MacArthur thought would help the war effort if one ever came.

Eddie had great pride in his 57th Philippine Scouts. They epitomized his philosophy on the blending of the two armies. There was a 10,000-man Philippine division of the U.S. Army, and they were exceptional. The 31st Regiment was all Americans, the 45th and 57th Regiments were a blend of largely American officers and Filipino soldiers. These special soldiers were called "Philippine Scouts" and were considered some of the finest soldiers of that time. They were crack shot marksmen. Eddie once said the Japanese would quickly learn to respect them because "they were fighting like madmen!" He had once commanded a company of the 57th Philippine Scouts.

14

With MacArthur in command, finding the dope, as Eddie called it, became more and more difficult. "Dugout Doug" as the men liked to call him on Bataan, made very few public appearances and any news that came from his office was censored by his staff, who were handpicked by MacArthur, whether they were competent or not. "All was well," they consistently communicated, except in early July of 1941, the blackout practices began. Within a month, blackouts were practiced regularly, sometimes all night.

Eddie read the Philippine and Japanese newspapers, and even though they were full of propaganda, he read them thoroughly including "between the lines."

He went back and forth. One day he read that the Japanese civilians were starving because of the American blockade, and he boasted, "We are going to lick them without dropping a bomb!" Then the next week he noticed Manila harbor hadn't seen Japanese ships for weeks, and he would repeat his mantra, "We have nothing they need. We are too much trouble to attack."

In late September, 1941, he was made an inspector in the Inspector General's office of the Philippines Department. His duties included organizing the transport of military equipment over Filipino roads. These "roads" were constantly jammed with carts and carabao. If this task wasn't daunting enough, the control of the alien population was.

The German population had dwindled, but there were still over 1,000 Germans. The biggest problem was trying to tell the Japanese, Chinese, and Filipinos apart. The Chinese were the largest Asian minority in the Philippines. The Chinese didn't worry him because they had assimilated into the Filipino culture. It was the 50,000 Japanese on the islands, and of that number, 10,000 were not naturalized. But this didn't frighten Eddie.

The shrill scraping of metal on metal and the shifting of clammy bodies trying to stay standing woke Eddie. He was immediately disoriented, but the oppressive heat and vile smell brought him back to reality. The boxcar had stopped, except for the shifting and pinging of gears and levers. From the doors, he could see only jungle. Everyone was ready to get off the train, but no one was sure what they would see once they jumped out. It was like suspended animation. Your body said MOVE, but your brain said WAIT.

Eddie imagined O'Donnell and what it should look like once they got out. The Japanese should have been working diligently for the past several weeks to prepare for the influx of prisoners making their way to Capas. Latrines should have been built within a short walking distance from the barracks. Water spigots should have been plentiful so men wouldn't have to wait in long lines for drinking or cooking. A hospital should have been stocked with medicines ready for all of the sick and wounded and needed by those with malaria and dysentery. Finally, there should have been food waiting for the men, either in a kitchen or mess hall. Eddie could already smell the hot garlic soup loaded with rice and chicken. The men would still be prisoners, but every attempt should have been made by the Japanese command to treat the men with respect and dignity.

Eddie was dreaming of walking the perimeter of Camp O'Donnell, stretching his legs, when everyone began to push forward out the opening of the rail car. The drop was a good three feet, and no one made it without tumbling into the gravel by the tracks, rolling into the jungle. Obscenities rained down as weakened men tried to stretch their numb and cramped appendages. One man hit first on his shoulder and cried out in pain. Several men on Eddie's car were pushed out but fell head first and didn't move. A handful of men were still in the car, unmoving, on their sides or leaning against the boxcar walls at bizarre angles. All of them appeared to be sleeping. Eddie knew differently.

Once Eddie was able to stand, he joined the other men and staggered toward Capas. They were a pitiful lot, filthy and tattered, but still strong enough to help those injured or sick disembark the train. There was even a palpable sense of optimism that maybe the worst was over. Things couldn't get any worse than their journey through Hell. Their situation had to improve.

16

If the local population's reaction at Capas, also known as Camp O'Donnell, was any indication of the prisoners' appearance and the horror that awaited them, it was very telling. Filipino women, children, and old people stood as close to the road as the guards would allow them. Tears ran down their faces as they stared at each man with shame and pity. Some tried to give the men foodstuffs or water, but if they were seen by the guards it could cost them their life. Cans of water were left by the roadside. Guards kicked them over as they discovered them. Many of the men who survived the Japanese would later claim the Filipino civilians had been their saviors.

The men were marched through Capas to an open clearing where the guards set up a temporary fence around them. There they were made to stand for the next two hours at midday under the broiling sun while the Japanese toyed with them. This treatment happened often with the Japanese, and the men had cynically named it "sun treatment." An old man with no teeth had removed the hat from his head and shoved it into Eddie's hand as he walked past the line of civilians by the road. It was sweat stained and stunk like oily hair, but Eddie smiled at the man and tried to wink a thank you. While standing in the clearing, the hat probably saved his life.

It was another seven miles to Camp O'Donnell, and every man did his best to make his feet move. No one regretted being out in the open with the fresh air churning through their lungs. But those last few miles seemed like an eternity for some of the men. Some collapsed in the dust, never to walk again. When the camp came into view, their poor hearts had to break when their eyes caught sight of the futility which was their future.

17

The camp that Eddie had imagined on the train was just that, a figment of his Western imagination — a naive dream. Camp O'Donnell was 615 acres with a perimeter of fortified rusted barbed wire. Over it all flew what the prisoners crudely called the "Flaming Red Asshole" or the Japanese battle flag. The men waiting for them at the entrance were earlier arrivals and looked like beings from another world. With emaciated bodies, mostly covered in rags, unshaven with unkempt hair, they gawked at the new arrivals with blank, empty eyes. Eddie stared back, realizing at that very moment how pathetic he must have looked as well. If the reflection in the broken glass was telling the truth …. Lord, what a frightening sight they must have made!

When he stared down to take a long look at his appearance, he saw his ring once again, shining brightly on his right hand. It wasn't hard to miss, for heaven's sake. It was gold and garnet in a background of brown and grime. He knew instinctively what would come once they arrived at the camp so it was time to hide the jewelry. If the guards made them remove their clothing or did a strip search, his earlier hiding place was no longer safe. Time for more drastic measures. Swallowing a ring this size was not practical, so his other available orifice would have to suffice. There would be time later to think of a more appropriate sanctuary.

It was at that very moment that a vision flashed through his mind. It was of one of his favorite photos of him and his love Nancy cruising around Staten Island in the summer of '38. It seemed like yesterday it was so vivid. She was wearing sailor pants and a striped red and white shirt to match with a flashy bandana and a wide brimmed straw hat to shield her beautiful face. She was sitting on his left knee as he smoked a cigar. His left hand cradled hers and they were both wearing their West Point rings. Hers was smaller for their engagement, but an exact duplicate of his own. He could still feel her leaning back into him as he held her close. They were laughing together and the memory made him tear up, it was so strong. In a moment he was back in Hell; actually he was at the very gates of that netherworld far, far away from his dear one.

Upon entering the camp, Eddie tried to take a closer look at his surroundings. But his visual assessment was quickly interrupted when everyone was told to empty their pockets. The men called it the "Shakedown!" If they had anything Japanese, they were shot where they stood. This included the "Surrender Flyers" that were dropped from planes. Many of the men swallowed the flyers or crammed them up their butts. His ring was safe.

The pompous, overweight commander of the camp, Captain Tsuneyoshi, stood on top of an old wooden box, but that was after he ate his breakfast in front of men that hadn't eaten in several days. The little man looked like a caricature with his too tight uniform. He tried to sound virile and brash but he came off as abrasive and hoarse. He had obviously given this speech many, many times and its authenticity had long since faded. He looked ridiculous really, but the guards standing with their guns at the ready forced the prisoners to pay heed and listen. The rules at Camp O'Donnell were demeaning and humiliating, but after the recent search and seizure process, no one doubted their gravity. In a nutshell:

1. Always salute and bow to a Japanese soldier regardless of his rank and for as long as you can see him.
2. Anytime a Japanese soldier talks to you, stand at attention and say "Hai" which meant "Yes Sir." Refuse and you die.
3. Always remember the Japanese did not sign the Geneva Convention; therefore, they could do whatever they wanted to do to you.

Any pre-conceived notions you might have had that your

situation was going to improve were quickly extinguished. Where do we begin, thought Eddie, *now that we have arrived?*

18

There were 60,000 prisoners at Camp O'Donnell—50,000 Filipinos and 10,000 Americans. Many of the American soldiers had only been in the Philippines for a few months. They had had no training or preparation for the situation they now found themselves in. Many of them were literally clinging to life after the march. Death was imminent.

Although Camp O'Donnell had multiple problems, the most significant was the lack of water. A human can live several weeks without food, but only a few days without water. There were only a few water spigots within the camp, and these were for thousands of men. Eddie waited in line at a spigot for over 18 hours one day. His thirst was so severe that even in the midday heat he was no longer sweating. His lips were swollen twice their normal size. He was lightheaded and nauseous. Of course he was dehydrated like almost everyone else in line. Thankfully, the men on either side of him were stronger and helped him keep his place in line.

If you needed water for cooking, you had to walk down to a stream or creek to collect it. Most difficult was remembering that anything you drank really needed to be boiled first because drinking bad water was a sure way to get diseases. Tell this to the young men who were desperate with thirst.

If their minds burned for water, then their stomachs screamed for food. It was this constant hunger and malnutrition that led eventually to almost every death. You were forced to eat anything you could find, particularly if it had substance and wasn't rice! RICE, RICE, RICE was all the men ate. If you could find things to cook with the rice, like small mammals, reptiles, or birds, then you got your protein and your stomach might feel full. The trick was cooking it properly and not eating it when it had gone bad. All these difficulties would kill you later, but when you were hungry and especially young and green, you just needed to eat! When your only thoughts were for food and not sex or women, you knew the men were literally starving to death. There were several items even starving men at Camp O'Donnell refused to eat... geckos because they ate mosquitos, and the camp mascot, an old bulldog, that everyone loved and watched after.

Malaria and dysentery were rampant, but dysentery was the worst. Caused by a bacteria or parasite, its victim suffered gut cramps and bloody diarrhea up to ten times a day. If you didn't have the disease, the odor alone would make you want to vomit. Plus, it was extremely contagious, so in tight quarters everyone would eventually get it. Housing was crowded. There were small huts built for 16 men that ended up holding as many as 40. If you had this debilitating sickness, you slept outside your barracks and as close as sensually possible to the latrines. Some men crawled under their huts and died there. No one knew it until a new noxious smell attacked your senses. Antibiotics cured dysentery—if you had them.

The men established two of the huts as a hospital and one was designated as the Z Ward or Zero Ward. This is where men went to die. Most of the men in the hospital ended up in the Z Ward eventually. But the men lying in the hospital were still itinerant. Most suffered from bouts of malaria or malnourishment. But with rest they might eventually be able to return to their barracks. Many were in the hospital so they wouldn't infect the other men.

Countless men in the Z Ward were crippled with severe dysentery and without proper meds were destined to die. They laid in their own feces, unable to get to the latrines, and waited for death. Swarms of Blue Bottle Flies were everywhere, including in the men's eyes and mouths. Called the "filth fly" because they would alight and eat anything dead or gross, the men were unable to control their numbers because everywhere you looked was repulsive and revolting. Wherever the fly landed before was then deposited wherever they landed next. This was how disease spread and men died. To see your buddies or strangers in this condition was disheartening for anyone. But even if you didn't visit the "Pest House" as the men called it, you could still wake up in your barracks every morning and have the dead sleeping next to you, only it was the eternal kind.

Men still had to be buried though and an area was designated for that very purpose. The Japanese wanted to cremate, but the chaplains convinced them to give space for burials. They finally agreed and even allowed the men to keep records of names and places of burial, unless you were executed or left camp and died.

If you were strong enough, you got the opportunity to do funeral duty. Blankets were thrown over poles and the corpses were shuffled to mass graves by skeletons still strong enough to make the long trek to the cemetery. Eddie tried to do this duty whenever he was able. If the truth be known, he had two motives. He wanted to be helpful and compassionate, he felt it his Christian duty. But he also knew that when you did burial detail, there was always a chance that you could pick up spare clothing or blankets. Eddie didn't want these items for himself. No, he knew men much worse off than he was and so he would bring back anything usable for those in need. It was a sad reality, but the dead didn't need them anymore.

It was on just one of these mornings that Eddie solved his ring dilemma. The day had begun hot and humid as always. The funeral dirge was a cacophony of cuckoos hidden in the nearby forest. Beautiful birds in the midst of ugliness and horror and still they made music. The four men shouldered the litter as if it weighed a thousand pounds. Their steps were slow and measured. The poor soul couldn't have weighed 75 pounds, if that. But Eddie and his companions were malnourished and hot with the sun burning down on them even this early.

When they got to the hole, they carefully removed the body from the blanket. It was so emaciated it was hard to tell if it had ever been human. Around his neck was a small leather pouch the size of a silver dollar. It was held by a thin piece of rope, possibly a shoe string. Eddie removed it gingerly and checked inside for any keepsakes. A small St. Christopher charm dropped into Eddie's outstretched hand. The tiny clasp had fallen off so the prisoner had fashioned the pouch with shoe leather to keep it safe. It was durable and Eddie knew immediately he had found a secure place for his ring. He took the broken charm of one of his own favorite saints and placed it in the dead man's pants pocket. He could keep his clothes today. Eddie silently gave him thanks for his pouch, as a chaplain said the Lord's Prayer over the hole in the ground. The man lay on his back with his face to the endless blue sky. Eddie made the sign of the cross and turned to see the next funeral detail coming along the dusty trail.

He was thankful, too, that today's funeral was in a single grave and not a huge pit. These were the worst because men were frightened by the body parts that could be seen sticking out randomly until the pit was sealed. It was a physical and psychological struggle to be constantly surrounded by death. No one was immune, and everyone could feel the shadow creeping up behind them. In the first 40 days at Camp O'Donnell, some 1,000 men died. Every day had lots of funerals. In the nine months of its existence, Camp O'Donnell killed thousands of men; some 1,547 Americans and over 26,000 Filipinos. These numbers didn't include the men that were executed or sent out for hard labor details and never returned.

19

There were many mind traps at Camp O'Donnell. It was surrounded by thick jungle. Where would you go if you did escape? Most couldn't speak the language, and the island was controlled by the Japanese.

One night on his way back from the latrine, Eddie saw a man sprint to the wire. Even though it was hard to see him, Eddie could hear the spikes of rusted metal tear at the man's clothing and bare skin as he made his way over the fence. He hit the ground with a thud and a grunt and high tailed it into the pitch dark jungle. The whole incident happened so quickly that Eddie had no time to react. He knew there were American and Filipino guerillas out there somewhere and the odds of the man finding and catching up to them before capture were slim to none. Eddie heard a few days later that an escapee had been brought back to camp tied hand and foot and dragged through the front gates. Those who knew him claimed torture had made him unrecognizable for several weeks.

Even though escape was virtually impossible because of where the camp was situated, men still tried. Though initially their captors didn't seem concerned about escapees, it eventually became a problem. Ultimately, a number system was used to deter escape; it was a warped and intimidating punishment. Every prisoner received a number. If a man was able to escape, the men five numbers above and five numbers below were killed. This method was definitely effective. And to be sure this scenario rarely played out for real, a responsible man from the group was assigned to keep track of the other ten men. The Nazis used a similar form of collective punishment. If you escaped and were returned alive, you chose another prisoner to die with you. If you refused the guards might kill fifty men and you. If you were caught escaping you were going to die regardless, but to take an innocent man with you was a whole different ball of wax.

20

On June 1st and 2nd, 1942, the Americans were transferred to Camp Cabanatuan. The camp was less than five miles from the town of the same name. Manila sat sixty miles north. Bataan to Camp O'Donnell took several weeks, but O'Donnell to Cabanatuan took about four days. Those able, walked; those unable, rode trucks. Camp Cabanatuan was the biggest POW camp in the Japanese system. If you counted "the Farm," it was 400 square acres. Camp Cabanatuan was surrounded by barbed wire and plenty of guard towers. All told, there were some 9,000 prisoners of war in Camp Cabanatuan.

Out of fear of disease, the Japanese separated their own quarters from the prisoners with a large neutral area that served to divide the camp into two sides. There were areas for a hospital, and once again a Z Ward was set up for those dying of the communicable diseases. The hospital saw all sorts of maladies including malaria, beriberi, scurvy, pellagra, and pneumonia. Then there was the infamous Farm. With an enormous vegetable patch encompassing three quarters of the camp, the Farm grew yams, corn, beans, garlic and any number of crops to feed the Japanese soldiers, not the prisoners. Over two-thousand prisoners, divided into gangs of 100 men, shoveled, planted, pulled weeds, and harvested plants they would never consume. That is unless they stole something. Not many tried theft for the cost was too high—a beating, solitary confinement, or worse. Men worked from six in the morning until eleven at night with no shoes or proper clothing. In the dry season, they had to carry five gallons of water back to camp at the end of the day. Daily beatings and random punishments made farming at Cabanatuan dangerous duty.

Upon arrival, everyone was strip searched and that included probing body orifices. This was mortifying for the prisoners and nauseating for the guards. Still, men were brutalized and the Japanese weren't concerned about first impressions. Eddie hadn't been shocked when the order came to move camps, but when the walk began from Camp O'Donnell, his ring became his focus once more. He knew the Japs wouldn't miss a chance to take trophies. It was imperative that he find a new hiding place. There really wasn't a place on his body that felt secure, nor was hiding the ring in the jungle a possibility. The ability to return and retrieve the ring was possible but scarcely certain.

The Japs gave very few rest stops, but on one of them,

Eddie made sure he couldn't be seen. Most men sat on their haunches whenever they rested, if they were still physically able. This Asian habit suited one well when there was no place to sit. The ring was huge and bulky, especially in its leather safe. Eddie's fingers were meat hooks, developed through his athletic career, and even more so now that they were swollen. Eddie's feet were large as well for this once hulk of a man, and his boots were still in one piece. He would have to try and tie the ring into the inside of his boot along the lace holes. The pouch was flung into the jungle. He could always craft another one later, once they had established themselves in the camp. For now, his new safe place would serve him unless the Nips made them remove their boots. It hurt his foot to have a bulky piece of metal tight against the arch of his foot, but it would only be until the search was over.

Later, he would retrieve the ring and work on a new spot to serve as a receptacle. Under different circumstances, all this trouble over a single replaceable item would have seemed ridiculous. However, the ring had turned into a portal to memories of home and the past. Whenever Eddie touched it or looked at it, he could see Nancy and his son in his mind's eye. Maybe it was malnutrition and disease that had heightened his senses, but whenever he thought of them he had a renewed sense of optimism and hope. He could smell Nancy's Chanel perfume and Johnny's blonde tousled hair when he pulled him from his crib every morning. It was urgent that he hold on to this ring. Sometimes he felt like his life depended on it. He would go home with the ring someday, and Nancy would be there to welcome him, wearing her own matching ring.

Eddie had been searched by the Japanese before, along the march to Bataan. These guards seemed new at the whole process and consequently a bit more tentative. He had a bit of luck when the man before him lost control during the anal probe and spurted the guard with excrement. The guard screamed "Buta" (pig in Japanese) and shoved the offender tumbling towards the waiting barracks. Eddie stood tall, looked him straight in the eyes, and called him "Sa" (Sir in Japanese). The guard checked his pockets, found his rosary beads and handed them back. He removed Eddie's hat, and finding nothing, waved him on. Eddie's Japanese was pitiful but he had picked up a few useful words in the past couple months. Today his new knowledge had served him well. The ring was safe for a while longer. He would find a more comfortable spot once they had been assigned to a barracks. Later, when he removed the ring, a bruise covered the top of his left foot. For now, the ring would stay in the cuff of his shirt, rolled up at the elbow. It was a lot of trouble, he knew, but he didn't care because all the pain and worry was worth it.

The barracks were bigger here at Camp Cabanatuan, but there were also fewer men. There were men with serious dysentery who couldn't stay in the barracks but rather had to reside in the shadow of the latrines. Eddie had had dysentery on and off during the last three months. For now, he was able to sleep on the floor inside the dwelling.

The morning after their arrival, Eddie walked slowly around the camp to get a better look at his current situation. There were men that Eddie had never seen before. They hadn't been at Camp O'Donnell, of that he was sure. Their faces weren't as drawn; their clothing not as tattered; they didn't stagger; their eyes still had a spirit. Eddie and his fellow prisoners were the walking dead — zombies really. He didn't have to ask to know that Corregidor had fallen. He knew these men had spent the past months fighting to keep Corregidor from the Japanese. Thankfully they had held out longer on the "Rock," the "Gibraltar of the East" than we had at Bataan. Its fortifications, the Malinta Tunnel, and strategic importance at the entry of Manila Bay made its continued existence as an American station imperative. The Japanese were too powerful and their weapons too advanced for our soldiers and Corregidor fell on May 6, 1942. Just those few short weeks had given these prisoners a visible advantage over the Bataan POWs. There were some with arms in slings and burned faces. But these men had had a month's worth more food and hadn't had to walk for miles. They didn't have to endure the atrocities—to gasp as their friends were run-through, beheaded, or buried alive. They had not yet had to soil themselves or wake up at dawn with their dead friend's hollow eyes returning their anguished stare. Just a mere month had saved them from these horrors. The challenges of prison life under Japanese control debilitated one quickly.

Later, Eddie was livid when rumors claimed that the doctors from Corregidor had brought medicines to Camp Cabanatuan. These meds would have saved the lives of many diseased men. But they were sold to the highest bidder! In Eddie's mind this was inexcusable—a mortal sin, an act of treason.

2 2

All the prisoners, including Eddie, were uncertain of their new abode. All of them tried not to think about how long they might be here and, if the truth be told, they were still hopeful that the American army was planning to come save them. There was no real news from the outside, except for the occasional glance at an English-printed Philippine newspaper. The tabloids were full of Japanese propaganda so the men could never be 100% sure that the counter-invasion wasn't being planned and engineered. As the days, weeks, and months went by, the men began to settle into the boredom that was life as a prisoner of war. Randomly, the Japanese would grab a group of men and take them to build an air strip or repair a road. Eddie was fortunate and thankful to never be chosen for this duty. The men rarely returned or were ever seen again.

They had all been warned on arrival that the 10-man punishment was in place, and anyone caught trying to escape was responsible for the life or death of his brothers.

There were other possibilities, too. Eddie would see this numerous times in Camp Cabanatuan. A soldier would get caught trying to escape. When the guards brought him back, everyone would have to watch his merciless beating. The kicks to the face, stomach, and ribs would have killed a normal man, but the prisoners weren't normal men. Even in their weakened state, there was still fight left in them, and whatever strength they had left they used to keep quiet and not cry out for the guard's enjoyment. Most were unconscious in a matter of minutes. Eddie marveled that men were able to take such violent blows and survive. But most did and were then dragged and tied to a pole where they were left for all to see — their limp, bloodied bodies prey for any guard that happened to walk by, always seizing the moment to throw a punch or slash the unfortunate remnant of a man. All of this was for show because after two days, they were carried to the cemetery and shot. Unlike the prisoners that died of other causes, the executed were buried in unmarked graves. Gone. Alone. Forgotten.

23

It was barely a month at Camp Cabanatuan when Eddie began to feel weak and tired. Normally an upbeat and optimistic person, he felt lethargic and unable to raise himself in the morning. This was not normal, and when he ran a fever and started having severe cramps, he knew he'd been struck once again with dysentery. Everyone in the camp had had it, and most suffered from it over and over again. So it was with Eddie, and this time it knocked him down for several months. The bloody diarrhea and constant trips to the latrine wore him out. His bung hole became a fiery, raw, infected muddle. Since this was his fourth or fifth time having the disorder, it took longer to recover. Who knew how he'd gotten it this time, but the fact that their diet was rice and dirty water was probably the biggest reason. No one had soap to wash their hands, and the men that prepared their food probably didn't wash their hands on purpose. He spent some time in the hospital but eventually kept close to the doors of the barracks so he could get to the pit quickly and renew his excruciating ritual.

24

By late fall of 1942, he was feeling back to his old self. For the Japanese, this meant he could once again work with the two to five hundred men that marched outside the camp every day to bring rice straw back to Camp Cabanatuan. This straw was sustenance for the herd of Brahma cattle that lived inside the camp. Sadly, the beef wasn't for the prisoners, but for the Japanese. Never mind that prisoners were guaranteed to have three ounces of protein a day—this rarely happened. Just looking at the cows made Eddie's mouth water. When his health returned, so did his hopefulness. Even this obnoxious slight by the Japanese didn't get him upset. He just thought about home and his little family, and some days he would even sing his favorite songs inside his head so as not to bring down the ire of the guards on him and his brother workers.

It was Eddie's positive attitude that caught the attention of a young Filipino woman watching the prisoners on their long walk to the rice straw every day. All along the route were vendors prepared to sell goods to the prisoners or the guards. But Naomi Flores wasn't just any vendor; no, she was part of the underground known as the Miss U group. Miss Dorothy Utinsky had been trying to get goods and money into the prisoners since her own husband had been taken to Camp Cabanatuan, only later to die there. Sadly, their attempts had been unsuccessful. The items sent in to help weren't getting to the men they were intended for. Naomi had watched carefully for several weeks, trying to find the right man to make a connection with, a man that could be trusted to keep a secret, a man that was willing to give his own life to help others. She found that man in Eddie Mack.

25

One day as the men walked back to camp with their itchy, cumbersome bundle of straw slung over their bony shoulders, there was a moment when they were able to mingle with vendors and purchase necessities. Naomi sold Eddie a banana for one peso. When he handed her the peso and pointedly said, "salamat," she handed over the banana and 10 pesos in change. Eddie looked up, confused, and met her eyes in a question. She handed him a loaf of bread and leaned in to whisper that the bread contained a note. She spun quickly away so as not to draw attention as she moved on to the other prisoners. When he got back to the barracks, he was happy to share the bread with his roommates. He was even more eager to read the note. The plan was simple but dangerous. It involved trust but great risk. If he were caught, he could die, but if he lived, he could help countless men. His decision took only an instant. Eddie was now part of the underground, and he'd never felt so excited to begin a new assignment. Never. Ever. This work would give him something to live for, something to focus on, something to get him home to Nancy and the boy. This was just what he needed to stay alive, to combat the endless boredom and hopelessness of daily existence and persecution.

That night in the barracks, with the insects chirping and the occasional Eagle Owl calling for his mate, Eddie took out his West Point ring. His fingers had swollen into a fan of flesh, but Eddie grasped the ring tightly in his left palm and closed his eyes. He remembered the night back in '37 when he had first met Nancy. It seemed eons ago but, in reality, was just five years. A brother officer was dating a gal who had a teacher friend. The friend turned out to be Nancy Hassig. Eddie wasn't a big fan of blind dates, but he hit the jackpot this time. The foursome had gone into the city and had dinner in Chinatown. Eddie sat next to Nancy throughout the evening and felt an immediate connection with her. She loved books and she loved to read. She had lived on her own in the big city and was quite capable of taking care of herself. And most importantly, she loved children. She loved teaching them and wanted to have some of her own as well. Eddie felt immediately that she was a woman after his own heart. They saw each other every evening and weekend after that night, and he asked her to marry him two months later. He had waited a long time for just the right woman, and he had no doubt that he had found her. This newfound love and desire was something that he had never experienced before. Together they would raise a family and travel the world. He knew Nancy would caution him to be careful with this new venture, but he was certain she would support his covert activities. Longingly, he put the ring back inside his shirt sleeve. His stomach growled unmercifully like it did every night before he slept. This night was no different—only tonight he had a smile on his face.

26

Being part of the underground was serious business. It meant Eddie was now fighting back as part of a resistance. Up until now, he had been fighting the Japanese in a non-confrontational kind of way. "I will live no matter what you do to me." But now his actions were intentional and subversive. If he were caught, no doubt he would be tortured and probably killed. He knew the Nips would do it slowly and as painfully as possible. They would draw out his life, then take it, then revive him again only to repeat the process to draw out the agony as long as humanly possible. He knew what they were capable of. He had experienced their "fun" on the Bataan Death March. But he also knew that the SEAs, the underground's favorite nickname for their captors (slant-eyed ants) weren't providing for the needs nor health of the prisoners, and many men were dying daily. If the Japanese were determined to let every prisoner die from disease and starvation, he was willing to help those on the outside make sure that the men had a fighting chance. God, someone had to live to tell their story. The danger was terrifying.

It wasn't only himself that he had to worry about. Everyone involved was putting his very life in jeopardy. Eddie knew up front that the fewer people that knew of the group's existence, the better. He was willing to take that chance, but the only people that would know about their work were the ones directly involved with it. It was imperative that everyone have a code name. No more Colonel Mack or Naomi. He would be known as Liver (which he hated with a passion) and Naomi would, henceforth, be known as Looter. He would come to trust and respect this girl as if she were his own daughter. Hell, he was old enough to be her father and yet this young thing put her life on the line to help this rag-tag assembly of American prisoners.

He didn't initially understand why any Filipino would be willing to risk everything to help these soldiers survive, but he knew their hatred of the Japanese was as strong, if not stronger, than that of the Americans. All of them had seen friends and family brutally die at the hands of the Japanese invaders. The Japanese treated the Philippine people like dogs, without honor or respect. They wanted to bring them in to the Empire when the war was over, but there was no doubt that it would be as their servants, slaves, and concubines.

Naomi had another reason for risking her life, as was

the reason for all who helped in the Miss U group. She had a love and respect for the United States of America. Not that the Americans had been good to the Philippines throughout its history, but rather because of the principles on which America was founded — those of freedom and justice. It was those lofty ideals that made each of them give up their livelihoods, their money — whatever it took to keep as many prisoners alive as possible. For some it would cost them their lives.

27

This is how the clandestine system evolved. Lt. Col. Mack (Liver) prepared a list of needs within the camp. Fred Threatt (Mango), driver of the carabao herd, dropped off the list at the Bridge on their way to town. Naomi Flores (Looter) picked up the list at the bridge and took a train to Manila. Looter gave the list to the Amusateguis (Sparkplug and Screwball). Amusateguis prepared money and supplies to send back to Cabanatuan. Looter returned by train to Camp Cabanatuan with the goods and dropped them at the bridge. Mango picked the goods up at the bridge and returned them to Liver. Liver got the goods to the proper recipients and divided the rest up fairly among those most in need. Brilliant in its simplicity, but chilling in its fragility.

For Eddie, life wouldn't have to change much. He would go about his business as usual, being upbeat and talkative with everyone, just like he always was. As Camp Inspector and Investigating Officer, he was naturally concerned about every man's condition in the camp. He not only knew about how they were feeling, but he also made it a point to get to know men and their families. Before the underground, he had only been able to pray for them; now he could actually get a letter to a loved one in Manila or get the medicine a man needed to heal. He would make his rounds as usual, keep an ear open, and find those most desperate. He would still be very wary and he would definitely keep praying.

28

For the Filipinos of the Miss U group, there was no life as usual. The Japanese were constantly looking for American sympathizers. They had Filipino collaborators listening and reporting anything unusual or out of the ordinary. They paid these traitors for their information, so Naomi and her friends had to be on the alert, always looking behind them, watching who they talked to and what they said.

The Amusateguis were a Spanish couple living in Manila. Ramon Amusategui (Sparkplug or Sparkie) was the brains of the organization. He pulled all the supplies together and got them to the train on time. Without him, the group would cease to exist. His wife, Lorenza, (Screwball) went out daily, door to door, to find willing sponsors for the money and supplies. This was precarious duty. She had to be sure that the people she called upon wouldn't turn her in. This was a constant, tormenting fear for her and her husband, who assisted her when he could. They so loathed the Japanese and the occupation that they eventually sold their car and had to walk miles to their warehouse. There was no doubt that they were committed to this cause. They sold their furniture, clothes, and ultimately her jewelry to help sponsor prisoners at Camp Cabanatuan. Lorenza personally had some fifty men that she gave money to every month. This was in addition to the work that she was doing with her husband.

Fred Threatt (Mango) was imprisoned at Camp Cabanatuan. He was the driver of the carabao team that left camp every day to bring back supplies for the Japanese from the town of Cabanatuan. These water buffalo needed frequent stops for water and to wallow in the creeks along the route. It was at one of these stops that the drop off was secured under a bridge. Mango would surreptitiously pick up the packet from under a rock and make his way back to the wagon. Most of the guards that traveled with the carabao caravan were derelict in their supervision and normally passed the break smoking their pitiful quality, foul smelling cigarettes or talking amongst each other. Mango was always on the alert. If he felt uneasy, if he sensed any sort of danger or something out of the ordinary, he would wait until the next day to make the pickup. This was perilous because he had to put the list under the rock on the way to Cabanatuan and pick up the goods on the way back to camp. Taking into account that this slight of hand was a daily occurrence for him, Mango faced incredible pressure to remain covert.

Consequently, his anxiety level brought him to the brink of exhaustion. He knew that he must be successful—the work was so important to so many. Lives were being prolonged or salvaged. So alert he remained, seemingly with eyes in the back of his head and ears that could detect a disturbance in the swarm of the ever-present flies and gnats.

Naomi Flores (Looter) was a native, about 19 years old, with long hair that she wore several different ways, depending on where she was. She lived in a barrio near the camp and had a friend with a four-month old baby. She would borrow the baby as part of her disguise and act as one of the vendors. The baby was always slung over her shoulder. If she were walking down to the bridge, she would wear her hair in front of her ears, hanging in her face. If she were walking in front of the camp, she always had her hair behind her ears. Looter had several helpers—Vangie and Josepha—and they would frequent the rock under the bridge and leave supplies, too.

Naomi also rode the train into Manila once a week. Manila was some sixty miles away. Every trip was roundtrip and carried the possibility of injury or death. The trains were always overflowing. The passenger cars were only for the Japanese and everyone else rode on whatever space was available—the cattle guard, the tops of the rail cars, over the couplings that connected the cars, or even clinging to the hand rails on the outside of the engine. If there were other cars without Japanese guards in them, people could sit in these. On her first ride, Naomi saw a small boy slide from the hand rails on a curve and disappear under the train. She heard his mother's anguished screams for many nights afterwards. After the boy's death, she was always at the train long before departure so she could get a seat inside, even if it was in a cattle car. Accidents were regular occurrences. Yet the trains remained over-flowing, no matter the danger. Naomi had to get the lists to Manila and the supplies back to Cabanatuan so the train was her only real option.

Naomi was captured and tortured three times. When she was arrested, she was always taken to Fort Santiago in Manila. She was never caught with evidence that could harm anyone. She was taken if she appeared suspicious or was in an area where the Kempeitai (Japanese Secret Police) were snooping around, gathering up civilians for questioning. One time she was locked up for a few hours in a closet with no light and made to stand until she was brought out for questioning. She was released within the hour. But the last time, she was tortured. A guard had noticed that she was riding the train regularly to Manila and had been seen in the vicinity of Miss Utinsky's home.

This time they wanted names. She never gave them what they wanted, but they still used a hose and forced water down her nose and into her throat to create the feeling of drowning. When that was unsuccessful, they hung her by her ankles and immersed her head in a pail of water. She knew that this would be the end. But she survived, only to have sharp bamboo sticks stabbed under her finger and toe nails. In between all these cruelties, they burned her legs with cigarettes and a hot iron. Still she withheld information.

One day, Eddie happened to notice her legs when her skirt slipped up just a bit. They were covered in hideous scars. When Eddie demanded to know how her disfigurement had happened, she laughed it off, not wanting to disturb him — a bad cooking accident. Naomi knew that everyone had scars — some could be seen, like her legs, and some were unseen, buried, hidden. Both were painful and would never heal. Eddie worried about her constantly and said so repeatedly in his letters to her. "Caution Looter, always be cautious."

29

This whole arrangement was remarkable because of what happened after the notes, money, and other supplies got into the prisoner's hands. Eddie would have the recipients sign a receipt for the goods, which would then be returned to the benefactor or sponsor in Manila. In this way, everyone knew that their gracious gifts had been received and, in turn, would continue to send whatever they could afford or whatever was needed.

A large sum of money was passed from Manila to Cabanatuan in this way. But what could the men possibly spend their money on? This was the most brilliant piece of the entire system. The prisoners used the money to buy goods from the vendors outside the camp. So the vendors made the money back. And if the vendors, like Naomi, were part of the underground, they would give the men more change than was warranted so they could buy more. It was a win/win situation for everyone. Only you had to be cautious. Eddie wrote to Naomi frequently, using their code names and code words, of course, and he never forgot to remind her to be vigilant. He also signed every letter, "God bless you and the group." "God Bless you for your work." "May God shower you with lifelong blessings" before finishing with "E. Liver." He did change his code name up every once in a while. Sometimes he signed "T19" which stood for Tackle, his position on the West Point football team, and 19 which was his jersey number.

30

Eddie's group wasn't the only force at work in Camp Cabanatuan. There were several other sub-groups run by his fellow officers. One sub-group was run by Lt. Colonel Harold Johnson (Makabuhay), who was in charge of the commissary. Makabuhay is a plant that grows in the Philippines and is often called the "Heavenly Elixir" because it is known to stimulate overall good health. Johnson was able to cook the books so the Japanese didn't notice when goods came in because they were on the invoice and had been ordered and paid for. Johnson was aided by another Filipino named Horacio Manolato (Mutt) who worked with Naomi and the Amusateguis in Manila. While Naomi used the carabao cart detail as her way into Cabanatuan, Horacio would bring letters, money, or medicines that he had hidden in coffee, black pepper, or cassava bags. His most ingenious trick was making a list of supplies that he knew he was smuggling in for Colonel Johnson. These would be on a regular invoice, and Johnson would just make it look as if it was part of the original order.

The other sub-group was run by Jack Schwartz (Avocado). He handled those items coming in and out of the hospital. Items might include medicines for dysentery, beriberi, and even diphtheria at one point. He could also ask Screwball to write a letter to one of his patients who had lost the will to live. There was no curing someone that was lonely or couldn't find the strength to go on. She always came through with an uplifting note and a few pesos to spend at the vendors. She never failed to brighten someone's day. Lorenza was tireless.

All three men were good friends, but what they did for the underground was top secret and never shared with the others. Eddie knew that the others were dealing in the dark arts and, as such, he knew that if the hammer fell, it would break them all. But they paid these perpetual fears no mind.

Eventually Eddie was dealing with checks because many of the men in camp had uncashed checks. Some were over a year old. Great care had to be taken so Japanese guards didn't catch anyone coming into camp with money. Some Marine had tried it and had almost been shot! Eddie insisted that all checks come through him. As camp inspector, he knew the men who could be trusted. He'd been an officer for 15 years and could distinguish between a true need and some tall tale for cigarettes! He also worried about stolen, forged, and worthless checks. He didn't want Looter or Screwball taking checks from unreliable sources. If he felt the prisoner was good for the money, the check cashing took place. Looter should work through him and it would be safer for everyone.

The same went for the prisoners Eddie helped in the camp. He couldn't stress enough the importance of giving him the names and contacts of true friends, not casual acquaintances. He passed these names on to Looter and Screwball as he wanted them to be safe when they knocked on doors in Manila. The dominoes were so very tenuous, and even one slip could cause the whole structure to come tumbling down. There would be no putting the supply chain back together once that happened, and real human beings would be crushed in the melee of the Japanese' arrests and torture.

It wasn't just money and letters going into the camp, as it turned out. Some poor guy lost his dentures. Fellows were always needing glasses, razor blades, and shaving cream or a special tool or utensil. It made no difference; whatever the men needed, the team would do their best to find and deliver it.

31

Eddie's position as head of the underground, on the inside that is, gave him opportunities and access to goods that others could only dream about. He never took advantage though. On the outside, he was considered almost godlike! His compassion and concern for all the underground volunteers and their efforts made him exceptional, extraordinary. That's not saying everybody loved him. It was hard being Camp Inspector and Santa Claus at the same time, but Eddie made it work.

There was no doubt that Eddie was probably healthier because of his work with the underground, but it was because of him that so many were provided with cigarettes, shoes, coffee, playing cards, and even a baseball!

Most men got shoes and clothing by seizing that of the newly deceased. Everyone was buried naked. There was always someone in need. Many of the men were only able to wear a scrap of cloth called a G-string, because their clothes had rotted. Eddie was a Lieutenant Colonel, and as an officer he had a second set of clothes that he had carried on the march. No matter how worn and tattered his everyday uniform got, he had the spare for the trip back to Manila at the end of the war. Still secreted, his West Point ring resided in his rolled-up sleeve.

Eddie always wanted to be on the up and up, so he never asked for personal favors or special treatment for his close friends. He broke his policy just once, and that was for a roommate that had a raging skin rash. The poor man was allergic to sulfa and there was no calamine in the camp. If calamine powder could be found, he was certain that the doctors could make a lotion that would treat and heal him. With this one exception, deliveries were made for specific men in need, and any extra was distributed fairly and judiciously. Eddie saw to that.

The Red Cross sent packages, but they rarely found their way to the prisoners. However, for Christmas 1943, the Japanese were generous, in a matter of speaking, and passed out the packages. For the next few weeks, the men received a total of four boxes. Most contained food stuffs, and everyone was hungry! Trading even became possible. Some men ate too quickly and too much, and Eddie heard a Marine had died for this exact reason. His shrunken stomach just couldn't handle new food.

The boxes also contained sulfa drugs, so essential to combatting dysentery. But by February, most of the sulfa was gone, and Eddie knew that it had gotten into the wrong hands. Men were desperate for sugar and probably feigned diarrhea to get sulfa. They then traded with the Japs for sugar. Sadly, dysentery was a constant condition in the camp and sulfa could help immediately. Eddie felt certain there would be a reckoning after the war ended for these slimy individuals who thought only of themselves while others died. When the boxes were gone, the Japanese increased the men's rice serving and added some meat. The death rate plummeted as the prisoners got the calories they so desperately needed. Life in Camp Cabanatuan was as good as it could get in late '43 and early, early '44.

32

The life of any prisoner of war, no matter the conflict, was one of hunger, boredom, and loneliness. Eddie knew this to be true, but there were always other difficulties that made life miserable. In the Philippines, it never really got cold, but there was a rainy season. Not only was the continuous rain depressing, but the mud also made camp life insufferable. With no news coming in, Eddie begged Naomi for newspapers. If the men had no news, they made up their own. The rumors were so crazy that even propagandized news would be a blessing.

His background as a soldier cried out for routine, and Eddie made every effort to stick with any form of normalcy. He attended chapel daily if he could. This also gave him the chance to pray for others in the underground. He worried constantly for their safety, and never missed reminding them of the dangers inherent in their covert operation. "I say a prayer every day at the little Chapel for your protection, and we can't make it hard on the Lord!" He even asked Naomi to try and find communion wafers for the services.

Loneliness — overwhelming loneliness — that inter-
minable emptiness of memories past. He missed Nancy
and Johnny with a continual gnawing passion. When he
thought about them, his heart hurt and there was an immediate reflux response as his stomach turned into knots. He
and Nancy had been married only a short time when the
war came, but it was long enough to know that he wanted
to spend eternity with her. When the boy was born, that
love only grew. How he longed for a moment with them
now. He knew they were living with her parents in Kansas
City. Dr. Frank's huge attic on the third floor was their
home. Johnny would be starting kindergarten in the fall of
1944 and he felt guilty for not being with him on his first
big day. He and Nancy had agreed that even though she
was an Episcopalian, she would raise their son as a Roman
Catholic. Whenever the Japanese allowed them to send
a note home, he reminded her of her promise. The notes
were seven "fill in the blank" and "circle the best answer"
questions. "I am interred at......" "My health is Excellent,
Good, Fair, Poor," "I am uninjured, sick in hospital, under treatment, not under treatment," "I am improving,
not improving, better, well," "Please see that......" "(Re:
Family)......... " "Please give my regards to..." When the
Japanese-issued POW card asked, "Please see that ...."
he always mentioned that he hoped Johnny was doing well
in church, learning the Catechism.

Heavy censorship was imposed so the men had to

be careful in their remarks. Initially, the men got one card a month to send home. Later, they got four cards a year, but now they answered where they were interned, the condition of their health, and a 50-word message. If you weren't careful and went over the maximum, the yellow bastards just threw the card in the trash. There was a warehouse somewhere close by that was full of letters from home. Unfortunately, there weren't enough Japanese censors to peruse all the mail.

Some men got mail intermittently, and others never got a single note from their loved ones. Eddie only received a few of Nancy's letters, but he knew in early 1944 that Johnny was having eye surgery to correct his crossed eyes. He was happy to hear from home and he knew Nancy would be strong and reassuring when Johnny went under the knife.

Despite her letters, there was a perpetual nagging apprehension that never left his side. It was his constant companion. Were Nancy and Johnny safe? Did they have what they needed? He felt sure that her parents would take good care of them, but he could never be sure — this was wartime. He knew that if they were struggling, logically he could do nothing about it. But such is the pain of a soldier trapped as a prisoner of war. All he wanted to do was go home to love his wife and son. They never left his mind. Once reassured, he would immediately return to combat duty.

He had a garden that he tended near the barracks, and in the evenings, he would cook for his roommates. One of the ways men were able to escape the boredom, hunger, and loneliness, if only briefly, was to read. Some benevolent, gracious bibliophiles back home were able to get boxes of books into Camp Cabanatuan. The men were able to create a library of sorts. It wasn't populated with raggedy tomes from the 19th century, but rather a collection of the New York Times' best sellers from 1941. Every man had his favorites, and by the time Bataan was recaptured, these books had become raggedy, too.

Eddie read every book he could get his hands on. Some of the barracks had electricity so you could even read after dark. His personal favorites were *The Robe* by Lloyd Douglas and *The 7th Cross* by Anne Seghers. The first was set in the time of Christ and brought a lump in his throat every time he read it, which he did over and over. The second was about a man that escapes a concentration camp in Hesse. Germany was a long way from the Philippines, but the story gave Eddie knowledge about the other war, and his empathy for the main character was heartfelt.

All the men were particularly taken with a ghost story entitled *The Uninvited* by Dorothy Macardie. It was so popular that its pages had disintegrated by the summer of 1944. It was probably one of the finest books ever written in its genre. Whether the books were fiction or non-fiction, they were a god-send to the prisoners. They, if ever so briefly, kept boredom at bay and let minds drift away from this hell hole. The books helped keep the men's intellect working and reminded them that there was a world they hoped to return to soon.

Photographs

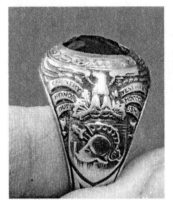 

Eddie's West Point ring, Class of 1925

West Point dress hat and Eddie's ring

Edward Clement Mack, Pennsylvania National Guard

Eddie and Nancy sailing in New York Harbor (Note: they are both wearing their West Point rings on their left hands)

Eddie and Johnny swimming at the Officer's Club at Ft. McKinley

Nancy and Johnny saying goodbye to Eddie in Manila Harbor
May 14, 1941

Redacted letter from Eddie to Nancy dated February 8, 1942

Letter from Eddie to Nancy and Johnny on Easter Day, 1942

Letter to Nancy from the War Dept. stating that Eddie is now a
POW dated December 21, 1942

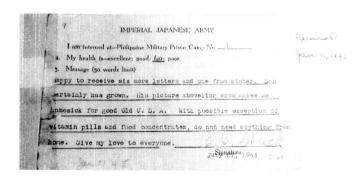

POW letter sent by Eddie to Nancy on July 27, 1944 and received
by her on January 11, 1945

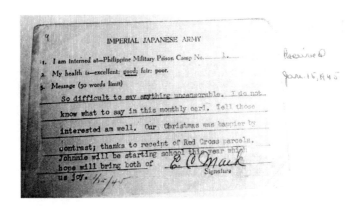

POW letter sent by Eddie to Nancy with send date but received on
January 15, 1945

Eddie and Nancy's son Johnny

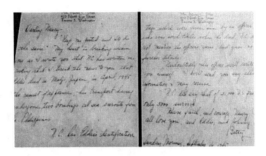

Letter to Nancy from Betty Pilet dated September 15, 1945 letting her know that Eddie is dead. (Note: this is two months before the War Dept. officially notified Nancy of Eddie's death

Letter to Nancy from the War Dept. confirming Eddie's death dated November 12, 1945

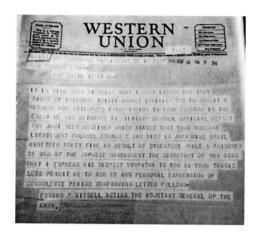

Telegram advising Nancy of Eddie's death dated November 16, 1945

Letter to Nancy from Gus Francis, Eddie's caretaker at the time of
his death, December 17, 1945 (this letter explains what happened in
Eddie's last days)

Letter to Nancy from General Douglas MacArthur dated
May 1, 1946

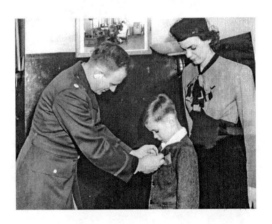

Lt. Colonel Harold "Johnny" Johnson presenting Johnny with one of
Eddie's medals posthumously (this happened five different times)

33

In early 1944, things began to get dicey for the Japanese. The sleeping giant had not only been awakened, but was also insanely pissed off. He was eager to unleash his fury and wipe out the Japanese, one island and atoll at a time. Starting with the Kwajalein Atoll, American Marines, under the command of Major General "Howlin' Mad" Smith, began amphibious landings that would eventually end the war in the Pacific. These attacks didn't just stop at the beaches, though the carnage there was impalpable. No, the Japanese were dug into the hills and hidden in trees and spider holes, literally waiting to die for Emperor Hirohito. They would sacrifice themselves with honor to fulfill that duty and take as many Americans with them as possible. This mentality of honor and sacrifice is what brought such wrath and disdain down on their prisoners who had disgraced themselves and their heritage by their surrender.

Every man at Camp Cabanatuan could sense the tide swinging against the Japs. Whether it was starvation rations imposed once again or brutal treatment by the guards for minor infractions, life at Camp Cabanatuan changed drastically. Eddie saw a guard beat a prisoner at the farm because he stepped on a new plant. The man fell unconscious, but the guard took one more kick to his ribs for good measure.

Eddie became overly protective of his people and warned them to listen to their guts when it came to their "sneaking" business. He had received several unsigned notes lately telling everyone outside the camp to be careful because they were being watched. If the pickups at the bridge felt "hot," Looter and Mango were to leave the packages for another day. If Mango delivered the goods and Looter was nervous, she was to lazily shake her head "No" at him. Mango was hard of hearing so visual signs were best. If he could not discern her signals, he was to raise his cap and she would sign again. Every precaution was to be taken for their safety.

The underground had been functioning successfully without capture or interruption for well over a year. It was a miracle since Eddie felt men were too loose with their talk. He feared the 5th columns collaborators in the camp—men that weren't pro-Japanese, but were so damned hungry, would report any suspicion for extra rice. The guards weren't always going to be unconcerned or inept in their duties. He had always worried that Mango or one of the women might get too relaxed and give the whole fragile charade away. And it was a combination of the last two that finally brought it all toppling down.

34

Looter had made the drop at the designated spot, under the bridge. When the thirsty carabao stopped for their daily wallow, Mango waited for the guards to take their smoking break. He walked nonchalantly to the spot and reached down for the onions, as Eddie called them. Mango had performed this exact move hundreds of times. It was always dangerous because, for those few seconds, he had to look down and away from the guards. It always made him sweat profusely and his heart would stop beating until the onions were safely in his shoulder bag. He would breathe a quiet sigh of relief and move back calmly amongst the carabao until it was time to head back to Camp Cabanatuan.

One day in May of 1944, he moved too quickly or took longer than normal reaching for the onions, and a new guard noticed a parcel quickly being secreted into his bag. Mango had just begun to breathe again when he heard a high pitched "Kisama!" He turned to see the new guard, green and oozing self-importance, running towards him with gun pointed. He tripped over the rocks once but kept his balance and rushed Mango, knocking him on his backside. With the gun stuck in Mango's gut, the guard reached out his free hand and asked in broken English "What you have?"

Mango knew the jig was up, but still tried to play stupid as he looked incredulously at the angry but unnerved guard. When the guard removed the safety, cocked the gun, and repeated "What you have?" Mango started to reach for his bag. The guard rammed the gun's muzzle into his lower stomach so hard that Mango grunted and lurched back in pain. When he regained his composure, he raised his hands in surrender, then slowly reached into his bag, his eyes fixed on his nervous foe, to pull out one of the onions.

In an instant, the guard tore it from his hand and ripped it open. Money, rolled in paper and marked with red signs fell to the ground, along with several letters. The other guards had walked over as the bust was going down and now looked at Mango with contempt and hatred. The oldest guard that had always treated Mango with some sense of fairness looked away from him, shaking his head sadly. Even he couldn't help Mango now. This situation was too serious and out of his hands.

Lots of yelling and Japanese cursing ensued, while Mango stood up and began re-harnessing the carabao for the long trip back to camp and certain death. He had a hard time holding his head up as the wagon moved in the direction of Cabanatuan. So far, he hadn't been hit by the guards. But he knew he was a dead man and everyone involved was now in harm's way and at grave risk. He had been careless somehow, and heads were going to roll. Literally. He looked along the trail for an escape possibility—there was none. He found it hard to look ahead as the trail disappeared with amazing speed beneath the buffalo as they prodigiously plodded toward the fate awaiting him at camp.

35

Eddie heard the loud swearing and angry Jap voices as soon as the camp gates were opened. He had lived this moment over and over in his most tormented nightmares. He had prayed at the chapel every day that this would never come to pass. When the Japanese pulled Mango from the wagon seat and began beating him around the head and chest with their rifle butts and truncheons, Eddie turned back towards the barracks and walked as normally as a condemned man could in this situation. The letter he had been penning to Looter was half finished. He picked it up and hand dug a quick hole in the ground to bury the crumpled piece of paper. He knew when they arrested him they would strip search him. He didn't know how long it would take the SEAs to decode the captured letters, but he knew his days, hours, minutes were numbered.

He walked to the chapel, removed his Rosary beads from his pocket and sat down on his haunches. He made the sign of the cross and closed his eyes while fingering the beads. He started the "Apostle's Creed," then "Our Father," and was on the second "Hail Mary" when his heart beat began to return to normal and his nerves to calm. When he had finished the Rosary, he fervently whispered the "Hail, Holy Queen, Mother of Mercy, our life, our sweetness and our hope!" Each line, thereafter, was said with passion, and by the last one "…through the same Christ Our Lord. Amen."

Eddie set his jaw, West Point to the end, and began to brace his mind and body for what undoubtedly lay ahead. He reached for the ring, still hidden inside his shirt sleeve, and placed it on his skinny finger. He had to hold it in place now so it wouldn't slide off. He thought once again of Nancy and Johnny and what they might be doing. It would be time for school to be finishing and both would be looking forward to summer vacation. With Johnny home, Nancy wouldn't have time to dwell on her loneliness and life without him. She understood her potential plight when she "signed up" with Eddie, just as certainly as Eddie understood his pledge to live by the inscription atop his ring — Duty, Honor, Country. She would put all her strength into getting more infor- mation on the conditions within the camp and what the future might hold for him and the other prisoners. She would be the squeaky, un-oiled wheel that Eddie had fallen in love with — and now he felt certain he would never see her again.

He knew what he had to do. It was time to hide the ring somewhere away from his own body. This pained him greatly, but he knew the Japs would strip search him when they came for him and violate him everywhere. The ring would be safely buried, a little deeper than the letter, but in a spot he would remember. He would survive whatever was coming and wear the ring once again.

36

When the guards came, they took not only Eddie but Harold Johnson and Jack Schwartz. All told, about twenty men were taken initially to the guard house where they were questioned, beaten, and tortured for the next three days. All were then released except for four men, including Eddie and Fred Threatt (Mango). The Japanese brought in investigators. Not only were the Japanese embarrassed by an underground working right under their noses, but they had more important things to worry about—like losing the war.

In all the time Eddie spent in detention, he never once gave anyone up, no matter how hard they beat him (sometimes he felt as if he would die). Despite the interrogator, he repeated his name and rank over and over like a chant. No matter what they did to his fingernails, his skin, and his knees, the thought of never seeing his family again was excruciatingly painful. When they bored of hurting him with no results, he was sentenced to four months in solitary confinement. This would have broken most men, but not Eddie. He had two forces at work in his favor. He had his God and he had a photo of Johnny that the guards had not taken from him when he was strip searched.

37

While Eddie waited alone in his cell, he agonized over his friends and what might be happening to each of them. The Kempeitai wasted no time dismantling the underground, piece by piece. It took them almost three weeks to find Ramon (Sparkplug), and on the morning of May 23, 1944, they arrested him in his office. They took him to his home to arrest his wife Lorenza (Screwball). For an hour, they rifled through drawers, broke furniture, and terrified the Amusategui children. The youngest was a mere three years old. The little son cried incessantly for want of kissing his Daddy. To no avail. The cold-hearted Japs ignored his pleas. When they found nothing incriminating, they dragged Ramon from his home without a touch or word to his wife or children. They would never see each other again.

Once in prison, Ramon was beaten, starved, and tortured. No matter how he was abused, he gave up no one. He kept telling the guards the entire operation was his idea and his doing—no one else was involved and no one else should be arrested. There was a witness that shared Ramon's cell. Ramon was to be executed on October 15th but promised the witness he would never give the Japs the satisfaction of beheading him. He died in the witness' arms on the evening of October 14th. They had shattered his body but never his will.

The Japanese warned the people of Manila from the beginning that their treatment would depend on the Japanese success in the war. Two and a half months after Ramon's death, a Japanese defeat was imminent. The iron fist came down and arrests spread throughout Manila, as promised. The members of the underground called it the "Reign of Terror." Lorenza (Screwball), Ramon's wife, had remained free and had moved in with her father. The Amusategui home was unsafe for many reasons, not the least of which was it had been bombed several times. When the Kempeinai came for her, there were twenty of them and they went to her old house. After questioning the neighbors, it took them another two weeks to find Lorenza's father's house. In that short time, she was able to burn all evidence that could possibly involve other group members. This was wise because on January 5, 1945, they found Lorenza and made a thorough search of the premises. They only held her for 24 hours. She was completely insane, or so the Kempeinai thought. Quite the actress, her dancing, singing, talking nonsense and making funny faces entertained and convinced them. She was no good to them. She was crazy.

Naomi had been watching from the safety of the jungle when the new and frightened guard intercepted the transfer at the bridge. She ran as quickly as the baby on her hip would allow her, straight back to the barrio. Her friend, the child's mother, was herding her other small children when Naomi handed the youngest over and ran for the back window. The Japanese were wasting no time searching the shacks, and she made her escape into the thick, emerald trees. She came to a lazy stream and immersed her shaking body into the spongy, muddy bottom. A lily pad over her head hid her from the Jap guards she knew were coming for her. What seemed like hours later, she stood, shaking, her raw and wrinkled skin tingling, and made her way back home. The authorities were waiting for her, in the dark. On this night, her hair was behind her ears, and she looked spent. The guards were antsy after waiting so long in her place and showed her a photo of herself, only with her hair down. They asked if she knew the whereabouts of this girl. Although she was relieved when she realized they didn't recognize her, she tried to remain calm and answered, "No." In the dim light of her apartment, and the lateness of the hour, the guards were satisfied, for now. After their departure, she gathered a few of her things in a pack, including all documents and letters, and set off for the mountains. She survived with a guerrilla group until the following February. Without a doubt, Looter was a fighter and a very lucky survivor.

Horacio Manaloto (Mutt) heard through the grapevine that they had been "given up." He hurried to find Looter to verify the terrifying information. She confirmed the prisoner had been caught red handed putting the package in his canteen pocket. The next day Horacio and two helpers were picked up by one of the camp officers and locked in separate huts in the camp. The friends were quickly released but Horacio was kept and tortured by the Japanese investigators. They wanted to know his connection with "Looter." No matter what they threw at Horacio, he denied any knowledge of Looter. The Japanese wouldn't give up. When he played dumb they would beat him unconscious and when he awoke he was thrown in his cell and told to think about it some more. After weeks of this treatment, he was released to go home. Eddie was not aware of any of this.

No news reached him in solitary confinement, and periodically the Japs would drag him out to inflict some physical horror to see if being alone had loosened his tongue. When this proved unsuccessful and they tired, he was taken back to his cell where he would try to heal before the next interrogation ordeal. There may have been one silver lining to his situation. He did get more food in his prison because the guards there were fed better. All told, Eddie spent approximately 120 days, 2280 hours, or 172,800 minutes thinking about the future and looking intently at the photo of his son. His strength and stamina before his confinement, his military training, and his ability to take his mind to another place made it possible to return alive to camp life.

After one such session with the interrogators, who never seemed to tire of trying to break his spirit, he thought back to a cool autumn day in October of 1924. He was part of history that day. He would play in a football game that would define college sports rivalries forever. The Army game against the undefeated Notre Dame squad coached by Knute Rockne was so huge they had to move the game from Army's home field to a different venue — the Polo Grounds in New York City. 55,000 showed up, and they weren't disappointed.

Eddie was a senior starting tackle and he lined up against Edgar Miller. That's Edgar not Don Miller who many know as one of the Four Horsemen of Notre Dame's backfield — so named that day by journalist Grantland Rice. Notre Dame won the contest 13 — 7, but Army was the only team to play them that close the whole season. At 5-2-1, Army was no pancake. Notre Dame would go on to win the national championship.

Eddie could still feel the bass vibrations of the drum line and hear the melodious flutes of John Phillips Souza as they marched the gray-clad cadets into the stadium. When the game finally began, he and his teammates were so wired that it took a series to calm their nerves and settle down to some bruising football. Eddie remembered the hits he gave and the ones he took. Each literally jarred his teeth. When the game was over, Army was disappointed in the loss but not ashamed of their effort. Eddie focused on the power and energy he exerted that day so long ago and drew strength from it many times before he was released.

38

When Eddie got back to the barracks, he was welcomed with handshakes and pats on the back. No one knew how he might fare after four long months. Their surprise and relief that he was still eternally optimistic cheered everyone up, but Christ did he need some soap! He realized this as soon as men began to back away from him after their initial contact, and they most assuredly told him why. He'd gotten used to his own stench and filth after so many months. Prisoners were a smelly bunch regardless, but crude bathing was allowed at Camp Cabanatuan, and Eddie needed a shower—yesterday. His smell was unearthly. After he cleaned up, he was updated on all the scuttlebutt, and to a man each was certain they were going to be shipped to Japan. This was not welcome news. Much discussion was had over whether going to Japan or staying at Camp Cabanatuan would improve their chances of survival. Most felt the Americans were only months away from arriving to save them. Freedom would come if you were still alive at Camp Cabanatuan. Only

God knew what could happen to you in Japan. Miserably, this wasn't a decision any prisoner would get to make. If you could walk, you were going to Japan.

Eddie had only a few weeks to write letters to Nancy and Johnny. Everyone was concerned that they might not get home from Japan, so they wrote letters and left them with the men that were staying behind. Those men eventually buried the letters. If guys had diaries, they buried those as well. Eddie dug up his treasured ring and once again rolled it in his shirt sleeve. Most were malnourished, if not starving, by the time the trucks came to take them the three hours to Bilibid prison. 1,619 men were loaded up, and 500 were left behind.

Eddie had deep misgivings about leaving Camp Cabanatuan. Americans were bombing Manila, and he was sure they would eventually come for the prisoners. Some were afraid that the guards might kill all prisoners before they could be rescued by American troops. Most frightening was not knowing what might happen in the Pacific, on a ship, in the winter. If you survived the American bombers and submarines, what would be your fate in Japan? Slave labor? Medical experimentation like the Japs had done to the Manchurians? None of this mattered. He was healthy enough to join the 1,619 and ended up at Bilibid.

39

Old Bilibid was a former Spanish prison located smack dab in the middle of Manila. It was initially used as a penal institution for Filipino criminals. With thick stone walls and intermittent guard towers, it was a formidable structure. However, it was closed because its condition was deemed unfit for the detainees. After the surrender of the Philippines in April 1942, the Japanese could have cared less about its supposed condition and used it until the end of the war as one of their 17 prisoner of war camps. Bilibid also acted as a transit point for prisoners being sent to Japan and other Japanese-conquered territories where slave laborers were needed. Whether working in coal, lead, or zinc mines, factories or on docks, the prisoners were treated inhumanely and brutally. No one wanted to stay at Bilibid unless it was to wait out the war. In the fall of 1944, prisoners were arriving from all over the Philippines for transport north. Such was Eddie's fate.

There was no reason to make roots at Bilibid. When the merchant ships were ready to sail from Manila with fleeing Japanese civilians, the holds would be filled with American, British, and Dutch prisoners. Eddie waited almost two months for his ship because the Americans kept bombing the hell out of Manila Bay. The prisoner ships couldn't get in to make their pickups. Right before Eddie and the others had left Camp Cabanatuan for Bilibid, 100 Dutch prisoners had arrived in camp. They had been on a Japanese POW ship sailing from Java to Japan. The ship had been bombed, killing 900 men, and the 100 were the only survivors. Most of the dead weren't killed by bomb shrapnel but rather had drowned because they couldn't get out of the ship before it sank. Eddie knew they were called "Hell Ships." He and the other men were going to find out real soon why these ships had become infamous.

40

On December 12th, Eddie got in one more shave and shower before leaving the following morning. Four officers were allowed to take their personal belongings in one trunk. The trunks were carried on a truck. Everybody else had everything on their back and everyone got to walk to the pier. Eddie was still in possession of his spare uniform and his ring.

As they walked the three miles, the Leyte campaign by MacArthur was winding down. The Japanese were so desperate that they had unleashed their kamikaze pilots. The light cruiser Nashville was hit, killing 130 men and wounding 190 more. In two days, the invasion of Mindoro would begin. It looked as though the war was entering its final months. All of this was unbeknownst to the wary prisoners who marched or limped through Manila that December day. The streets were busy with civilians, carts, and carabao. Spanish colonial buildings suffused with columns and lattice work still pleased the eyes. Eddie took a good look around and remembered its historic nickname, "The Pearl of the Orient." The fancy dressed couples and lavish cars were gone, but there was still an air of dignity in the way people carried themselves. Damned if the Japs were going to defeat their spirits.

Two months later, in February, 1945, MacArthur would take back Manila. "I shall return!" became the city's death knell. The Japanese would never surrender so they fought to the last man, but not before they raped and killed women and children. Civilians were barricaded in churches and burned alive. Over 100,000 civilians died. The city was razed and looked more like Dresden and Berlin than the jewel it had been before.

At first, Eddie was mystified by the smell of alcohol everywhere on the streets. It smelled like a hospital. Then he realized there was no gas so everyone was having to use alcohol as fuel to drive. Thread bare and thin, the Filipinos lined up on both sides of the street as the prisoners made their way to the water. The troops were a motley sight for sure. Many of the men had no shirts and their ribs stuck out like cadavers. Some wore shorts or what looked like diapers. Their knobby knees held up their toothpick legs. The Nip guards gloated over their hostages in front of the civilians, thinking the prisoners would lose face. The Filipinos only felt sorrow for the

Americans and hung their heads in sadness. The Japs could never quite figure out why they reacted this way.

When the men reached Pier 7 and their ship, they had to wait in the sun and heat for hours while Japanese women and children boarded and took their places on the deck. There were also merchant Japanese seamen who'd had their ships sunk in the bay. Later, the Japanese 4th Medium Mortar Battalion arrived—all 558 of them, with their baggage, followed by the loading of artillery pieces, several thousand cases of ammunition, gasoline, and four trucks.

41

The Oryoku Maru was a passenger liner that weighed some 8,000 tons. She was made for luxury cruises in the Orient. Eddie looked but could find no markings on the entire ship. This was frightening. The liner was painted a battleship gray and boasted anti-aircraft guns. The American pilots would have no clue that they were firing on American prisoners. The 1,619 captives were divided into three groups, and each was going to a different destination. Some were going to Tokyo; some were going to Korea; and the rest, including Eddie, were going to Kyushu. Finally, at dusk, the different groups were placed in each of the separate holds, three decks down from the main deck. Each held about 550 men. None had any ventilation or portholes. The only light and fresh air came from the 20-foot by 20-foot hatch.

As Eddie approached the hatch, he could see men hesitating as they looked down into the deep hole left by the open entrance. The Jap guards gave no one time to re-think going down the ladder. If you paused too long, you got a bayonet in the back. Eddie was always thinking logically because that's what his different jobs required. He was nervous. He could hear the drone of planes in the distance. He could tell, just by looking, that the hold was going to get crowded. He was truly concerned that there might be a problem getting access to water. The damned Japanese had just fed them a small meal of fish heads, rice, and salt with seaweed, for God's sake. Everyone was thirsty. They were always thirsty. This was bedlam in the making.

When Eddie finally got to the gaping hole, he wasted no time descending the ladder. There were men lying at the bottom with broken bones. They'd been pushed by the guards for being too tentative, too slow. A few rays of sunshine filtered down through the dust created by the meager straw left for bedding. He looked around to see the dimensions and figure the possibilities that the space offered. There were no latrines or buckets for waste. Men weren't able to sit on the floor but had to stand or sit with their backs against the wall. These poor men had others literally perched on their knees. Some arrangement would have to be made for changing positions periodically so each group could get a rest. It was already hot as Hell and everyone wasn't in the hold yet. This was madness. Quite literally.

42

Once everyone was loaded and stowed, Eddie knew they were in serious trouble. Of all the experiences he had had throughout the entire POW ordeal, this one was most likely to kill him. He could feel the anxiety welling up in the men around him; a panic unlike any other they had felt so far. They weren't afraid of the Japanese anymore. They were afraid of themselves, both inside and outside the ship.

After begging the guards to send down buckets for all the waste from so many men, four five-gallon buckets were lowered. Somehow, with cooperation, they were able to send them man by man and get them placed in the corners of the hold. The buckets were overflowing in a few hours. Urine and feces covered the floor, and once the ship began to move and vibrate, the filth covered every inch of their habitation. The stink welling up out of the holds was so pervasive that the guards closed the hatches and left the prisoners without light and fresh air. The temperature continued its rise and peaked near 120 degrees Fahrenheit.

No matter what fate had thrown at Eddie, he was able to "detach his mind," send it to an isolated dark corner and forge ahead until the worst was over. West Point and his years training on the gridiron and in the boxing ring had developed his self-control and a toughness of spirit. For three excruciating years, he had kept the faith and survived every inhumane horror and physical setback. His strength of character and dedication to the Army, belief in God and Country, and constant hope for a reunion of home and family had kept him living. But this? This was not the same. Seeing men beheaded by the enemy in light is unlike the deaths perpetrated by friends and fellow prisoners in the dark, this darkness that was a veritable ink well. There were warm bodies undulating in the gloom. They were opaque, like the hand you place directly in front of your face—blindness so complete that you were frozen in fear. This was Dante's Inferno, Poe's "Premature Burial." Eddie remembered reading about safety coffins and ringing a bell in his brain until its clanging fused with the ship's engines and the prisoner's panicked shrieks for help …. Help …..HELP! The vibrating ship did help some of the crazed men calm, if only because it forced them to focus on the noise. It was a mindless sound, yet strangely hypnotic. Some even fell under its spell and drifted away into an awkward, troubled, and convoluted sleep.

43

He was so thirsty. All he could think about was water. Water lay under them and rocked them incessantly, but even if it were attainable, of course it wasn't drinkable. Yet hearing it slapping against the hull only made the desire to quench his thirst that much more pressing. He must have water. His needs outweighed his very soul. Eddie thought of the ring, what he felt was part of his being, his wormhole to his family. What deal could he make that might allow him a few drops of the life-sustaining solution? That, at least, was the compromise his brain made in a trade for life. He could trade the ring for water. The ring was inanimate after all, a solid connection to the loved ones, but loved ones half a world away. It was just a piece of jewelry. With it, he had less of a chance of returning to them. With the water it might garner, he would improve his chances. Yes, the ring.

Eddie unfolded the tattered and almost see-through sleeve from his left elbow and fingered the hard, smooth surface—the small indentations of Duty, Honor, Country still traceable under his warm, dry fingertips.

A memory of the West Point formal dinner and ring presentation ceremony twenty years ago was so real it released him from his thirst, if only for an instant. A candlelit dinner, the presentation of his ring, and the promise of a miniature for his future bride were all part of this most-beloved ritual he shared with his classmates before their senior year. That night he became a firstie. He felt the pride of this ring given only to those strong enough of character to accept the challenge of a life spent in the military. He still had that strength, and his survival this long proved it even now. Would that same strength allow him to make a decision that would possibly save his life? It was time. When he returned from the cherished memory to the hellish reality that was the hold of the Oryoku Maru, he was ready, convinced of the correctness of this sacrifice.

Where was the young man? The one that offered water for a trade? The soft voice that offered life to anyone willing to trade? He was gone, vanished into the gloom that was their world at the moment.

At that instant, a giant explosion rocked the ship. Immediately, swearing at a frantic pace burst forth and now filled the blackness. Gone were the pitiful cries for water. Now only terror—sheer unadulterated horror as the ship pitched heavily and shuddered from bow to stern. Screams and blind pushing engulfed the ship's cargo cauldron as the human-like consignment tumbled through the pitch. Bodies slammed against flesh. Bones snapped and protruded. The stickiness that was surely blood sprayed from all directions. Those less injured tried to find "up." One Dutchman luckily found the ladder extending to the deck. He stepped heavily on something to gain the first rung. It brought a bellow from the unfortunate soldier whose head was his springboard. The Dutch soldier was pulled down by the injured man and by the many who tried to clamber past and fight their way upward as well.

Now a greater panicked confusion reigned. Eddie tried to make sense of all this. He could not tell if they were being attacked or doing the attacking. If the ship had been hit by planes, they would have had to have been American. Could they have drifted into a minefield? Maybe a submarine had stalked them and loosed a torpedo? Faintly he realized that they had to be the target—an unmarked ship with Japanese visible on deck. How would the American pilots know that the Japanese they saw were civilians, and their comrades were trapped below deck?

A flash of memory inspired by the current crisis recalled a conversation Eddie had with the Dutch sailors and their fear of drowning in the hold, not being able to swim to shore. Johnny, Nancy, death—what was to come? Darkness and chaos prevailed. Surely this was the end. Then a laser of light from above pierced the gloom as the hatch was thrown open. Nearly hysterical Japanese guards appeared and screamed for doctors. "ISHI, ISHI?" "Ishi must come deck immediately." Doctors were demanded. The SEAs were adamant! The few doctors housed in Eddie's hold tried to untangle themselves from the pretzels that were arms and legs. It took an eternity to get to the ladder and once there the doctors were cramped from lack of movement and weak from no water or food, yet they began to climb.

44

Seeing light, no matter how faint, and knowing there was fresh air coming in made the panic that surrounded everyone diminish for just a moment. Eddie shielded his eyes. It wasn't the sun; it was the hold. What in the hell? The floor was still coated with urine and feces. As the ship rocked in the bay, the fluid sloshed back and forth and comingled with fresh blood covering the men. They had been packed in like sardines but were now a jumbled mess. Eddie wondered if shrapnel had come through the walls of the hold after the explosion and ricocheted through this mass of soft flesh. Most men were trying to untangle themselves, hoping that they could some- how escape this death trap of captivity. They scrambled, careened and fought each other — they were in survival mode. Eddie saw bodies that had been at the bottom of the pile. They were no longer part of the fray. They lay still, twisted, not moving.

The guards up above pointed their guns into the hold. It had little effect. Now the ship lurched again, and the sound of steel on sand let the men know they had run aground. They weren't going to drown. Surely they would be allowed out of this netherworld.

Later, the doctors climbed back down the ladder. All ears were at attention when the doctors described the carnage atop the deck. Bodies were strewn everywhere, and they had been reduced to simple first aid since there was no medicine or dressings to help. The task was overwhelming. They described the injuries of the children. No matter how much you hated the Japanese, it was hard for any human, especially a medic, to see a mangled child. To the queries of the men, the doctors had not been told what was to become of the men in the hold. Their future was still unknown. Eddie knew one thing though, and he was sure there were other observant men still able to have the same thought. With American pilots precisely dropping bombs on Japanese ships, the prisoners' treatment would not improve. Eddie couldn't imagine how much worse it could get, but that was a reality the survivors would face.

Down in the hold, men could only sit or crouch in total despair—groans of pain and agony—those dying. The rattle of death grew once again. Eddie heard a young voice pleading weakly for his mother. As darkness approached, the boat began to move. It was being towed off the beach. The Oryuku Maru was listing heavily, but apparently was still seaworthy. Unknown to them, they were headed for Subic Bay on the west coast of Luzon. The hatch had remained open and for that everyone was thankful. No one could rest easy though. It was hard to forget that there were American submarines lurking in the dark coastal waters. Dusk and dawn offered prime hunting. Eddie couldn't sleep, although his body craved it. He was hungry and thirsty and his legs kept cramping up. He was despondent. He braced himself for a long night.

Sometime later, he heard movement on the deck above and decided it was the Japanese civilians being evacuated from the ship. He was never able to sleep but he dozed off and on, and try as he might, he could not keep at bay the fears of never seeing his wife and boy again. He tried to remember Nancy's perfume and Johnny's baby smell. It was impossible in this cesspool. He tried to remember spooning with Nancy when they were first married and the contentment he'd felt listening to her heartbeat, yet it was impossible in this iron chamber of horrors. He fumbled with his rosary beads. His prayers sustained him until morning.

45

When daylight finally came, there was hope that they would be next to be evacuated to safer quarters. One of the guards had confirmed this before dawn. But as was often the case with the Japanese, their removal was delayed for some unknown reason. Eddie sensed the hum of planes before he actually heard them. Those with younger ears had heard the sound and were filled with alarm. They were trying to move, get out, find their way to the ladder. There was no time. There would be no close calls on this run, only direct hits.

The sound was deafening, yet Eddie couldn't hear. The concussion from a bomb had burst his ear drums. When sound slowly filtered back to him, he "heard" what he saw. Total mayhem. Men were screaming obscenities and others were just screaming. The hold was full of smoke so thick that it was hard to access what had happened. Sulfite burned his lungs. When the air began to clear, he saw what was left of the platform that had been built in the middle of the hold to accommodate more men. It had exploded into hundreds of nasty wooden shards, now deadly missiles. Men had been impaled like straw penetrating telephone poles in a tornado. Most were dead, and for this, Eddie was thankful. What could be done for them after all? Eddie was untouched, at least physically. Oh, he had a few bruises, and he was ready to drink straight from the ocean when he escaped. And rest assured, he was walking out of this hell hole.

46

Eddie counted every dead, mangled body that the Japs pulled from the hold. In their hold alone, 300 men would not be going on to Japan. There were still many injured men that would need help as well. Those able began to climb the ladder, assuming they would be allowed to leave. Everyone learned quickly that this was not the plan. The first three men up were shot dead and fell back down into the hold, taking those behind them to the putrid floor below. No one moved. You couldn't shock these men anymore. They'd seen too much. They would wait. What else could they do?

It was late morning before the guards told the prisoners they could come up to the deck. Although it was difficult, everyone made an effort to stay composed as they climbed the ladder to the light. Once there, they were told to remove all clothing except their shorts, shirts, and shoes. They were to tie their shoes around their necks and swim to the shore. That's right. Swim 500 yards to land. Hell, most of the men could hardly walk once they had reached the main deck. Many stumbled and face planted trying to regain control of their legs and arms. Additionally, two days in an open latrine surrounded by dead men was something you didn't get over immediately. Now you were expected to swim five football fields through the ocean to what you hoped was safety. Eddie rolled his sleeve down and retrieved the ring. In just his underwear, it was hard to find a safe place to store it. So he put it on his middle finger and turned the stone in towards his palm. He wrapped his beads around the same hand. He would have to be vigilant.

Eddie could see a few life jackets and life boats still tied up to the side of the ship. When men made a motion to secure them for transporting the wounded or those too weak to swim, they were shot at. The ship was listing dangerously so men began to jump off the sides into water littered with dead bodies and floating debris. Some of the debris was big enough to hang onto and with work could get you to shore. Most men began to try and swim. There was a current that moved a few men out to sea. Unknown to all the swimmers was the invisible path the Japs had created to keep everyone where they could be seen. If you swam or the current carried you outside the imaginary boundaries, you were shot. Eddie had been an athlete and that included swimming. He was so relieved to be outside and in the sun and fresh air that he felt re-energized.

The first 100 yards were the hardest, but he took his mind back to hot Augusts and two-a-days at the Point. He might have thrown his guts up the first couple practices, but he'd made the starting team three years in a row. He'd found his stride on the football field and he'd make it to shore now, despite the yellow bastards' attempt to kill every one of the prisoners. Right before he reached shore, he noticed something that made his blood boil and his arms pump that much harder. Floating in the water were cans of condensed milk, meat, and chocolate bars. Obviously, these were from Red Cross packages. Surely these items were intended for the prisoners. And most certainly the Japs had no intention of these being used by anyone other than Japanese civilians and wounded Nips. Eddie's knees hit sand. He had never been so glad to kneel on solid ground as he was at this moment, and he collapsed. The American bombers would come back in waves that day, and the Oryuku Maru would soon rest in Davey Jones's Locker.

47

Once on shore, the surviving 1,308 prisoners were marched to a concrete tennis court and surrounded by guards. They stayed there for five hot and cold days. It was crowded on the court, but at night when it got cold, the men huddled together for body warmth. During the day, it was like old times with the Jap's typical "sun treatment." Raw rice and three tablespoons of water were handed out once a day. Everyone had diarrhea again. Many of the men were almost naked after the bombing and swimming. On the third day, the guards gave these men a pair of pants and a cotton undershirt. They also asked one of the American officers for the fifteen most wounded men. Under the auspices that they would be taken back to the hospital at Bilibid, the men were selected. Many of the prisoners, including Eddie, were concerned for the fifteen. After all, why would the Japanese choose such a small number when so many were in critical condition? It was true these wounded wouldn't make the trip to Japan, but there were hundreds more in similar shape. Eddie had a bad feeling and although he would never know it, the fifteen were taken to a cemetery and beheaded or run through. Thrown in an unmarked grave. They never saw Japan or Korea.

When Eddie and the other prisoners were finally moved from the tennis court, they came to a school yard, then to Fort Wallace, and finally onto a beach to wait in the hot sun. Food and water were scarce once again. No one ever got an opportunity to take a long drink of cool water. The precious fluid was handed out in canteen cups for not one but two men to share. Eddie saw several crazed men succumb to thirst by guzzling water from the sea. Vomiting and delirium set in quickly and without fresh water to negate the effects of dehydration, they were gone.

On Christmas Eve, everyone was loaded onto trains for the trip to San Fernando, La Union. For three days, they rode with no fresh air in sealed box cars. Eddie had been here before, long ago, on the ride to Camp Cabanatuan. The only difference this time was the men had reached their limits long ago. They were only surviving because their poor emaciated bodies had refused to give up. They were all comatose on the train ride. Eddie slept the sleep of the dead. No dreams, just nothingness.

48

On the morning of the 27th, the train stopped, the men fell out of the cars, and stumbled to the pier. There were two ships waiting for them, the Brazil Maru and the Enoura Maru. This time the boarding would be tricky. Landing boats took them out to the ships, but the men had to jump twenty to twenty-five feet down into the boats from the pier. No ladders, just a bayonet in your back if you dallied. Men broke brittle bones on landing. It was a two-story jump.

Once on board, they were overcome with the reek of horse shit. The Japanese had previously hauled horses or cows, and of course they had not cleaned out the holds. Piles of manure smeared the rusted floors of the quarters where the men would stay until the 9th of January. There was more room for the prisoners on this leg of the journey, but there were three days when they had no water and five days when they had no food. Eddie thanked God the days were never back to back.

On the 6th, the ships arrived at Takao, Formosa. The men were sick, hungry, and begging for water. They were made to wait on the ship for three more days. Too long. On the 9th, the American Dauntless bombers hit once again. Eddie was on the Brazil Maru, and the Enoura Maru took the bombs. 300 men died instantly when hatches blew off and landed on stunned men. A floor collapsed and prisoners fell three to four stories to their deaths. Those men that lived had suffered wounds that only medicine and bandages could aid. Neither were available. For three long and torturous days, the living and the dead were made to stay on the ship. When Japanese doctors were finally sent in, they refused to look at anyone with more than an abrasion or surface wound.

On the 12th, the dead were removed from the Enoura and either burned or buried in a nearby mass grave. The wounded were pulled from the hold with ropes and no litters. They were loaded by hand on to rafts that took them to the Brazil Maru. Eddie watched from the main deck of the Brazil. God, he hated being on the water. If he'd loved water, he'd have been a squid in the damned Navy. One look at the ship and he could see it was no different from the first two. There were no markings, so the same dangers that had followed them since they'd left Manila were still chasing them. Only now they were headed north into winter, and it would be cold, so very cold.

49

They left Formosa for Japan on January 14, 1945. For the next 17 days, it was, in a word — attrition. It was crowded, but more bodies meant more warmth on the steel floors of the hold. It got so cold that there was ice and snow on the bottom decks, and most men had very little clothing. Everyone was hacking and coughing. Sanitation was horrendous; really non-existent. They were not even provided buckets for waste. They were given very little water, and when they did get water, it was often so filthy it was undrinkable. Eddie was thirsty though. The water didn't have to be pristine, and men put all caution to the wind when it came to anything liquid that even looked like water. Once again, men were suffering from diarrhea and dysentery with no meds to help them.

Eddie, Jack Schwartz, and Harold Johnson tried to stick close together and watch out for each other when they could. Two times on the journey the men were all told to remain perfectly quiet down in the hold! This wasn't too hard. Most of the men were incapable of moving around much anyway. They were too weak. Later, they learned there had been a possible submarine attack. Everyone's nerves were on edge once again.

It was after one of these incidents that Eddie and Jack made a pact one night. Both men were very realistic about their chances of survival. They had made it this far and were still alive, but they had no doubt that at any moment they could be fish food at the bottom of the sea. It was agreed that if only one of them survived, he would go to the other's wife and personally tell her what had happened. They shook on it. Just two old friends who hoped their promise would never come to fruition because they would both come out alive.

After seven days, the dead began to pile up once again. The men who had been wounded on the Enoura Maru were the first to die. Others died from exposure. By the end of the trip, twenty to thirty men were dying every day. Their bodies were thrown into the sea. To the men who knew them, they were no longer recognizable. They were literally shadows of themselves. There was no service, no memorial. Eddie prayed with his Rosary beads every day for those lost.

The ship did carry a secret that ended up saving some men and killing others. One of the prisoners was snooping around when a cargo of sugar was found in the hold directly below where the prisoners were being held. If he had been caught stealing it, he'd have been shot, but the Japanese were terrified of catching dysentery and so many other deadly diseases that they overlooked the pillaging of the sugar. They never got real close. Some men could handle the heavenly sweet grains and others couldn't. It gave many prisoners horrible diarrhea, but it could also keep you alive.

50

When they finally arrived in Moji, Japan on the island of Kyushu, there were some 500 survivors of the original 1,619 that had left Camp Cabanatuan. Eddie was one of the living, and though he had once played tackle and been a boxing champion, he now weighed a mere 125 pounds. He counted his blessings though. He was still alive, and he still had his ring and his beads. He knew that the war had to be drawing to a close. Why else would the Japanese have moved prisoners away from Camp Cabanatuan and all the way north to Japan?

He was beginning to feel that the journey might be coming to an end. It was a new year, 1945. He would be with his family next Christmas. As he waited on the deck to go ashore, he thought about the Christmas of 1939 at the Hassig's in Kansas City. Nancy had taken him proudly home to show him off to her family and friends. The dinner at Dr. Frank and Carrie's had been lavish and extravagant. Vergie, the Hassig family's cook, had prepared her usual sumptuous feast for an army of family.

The heavily laden table was candle-lit, and every family member in the city had come to celebrate Christmas and meet Nancy's husband and young child.

On the day they'd left to return to New York, Nancy's Uncle Charlie had made them stand on the porch, in the morning sun, as he shot a movie of the two of them standing hand in hand. They moved to the sidewalk and walked little Johnny in his carriage. God how he yearned to be with his family again. It made his heart hurt just thinking about them. He turned his hand over and stared at the ring once again. He noticed the garnet stone had chipped. When had that happened? Lord only knew with what he'd experienced thus far. He'd have the stone replaced when he got home. He shuffled behind the others in line to a building where men appeared to be receiving clothing. He smiled, another blessing.

51

Eddie collected what the Japanese considered winter clothing. Every man was issued a pair of underwear, an undershirt, pants, and a long-sleeved shirt. It wasn't Brooks Brothers, but it was better than nothing. He was thrilled when he realized he had a hiding place once again for his precious ring, and wasted no time making the switch. He was fortunate to still have shoes because even though the Japs passed out sandals, some men were barefoot.

Jack Schwartz had done Eddie's surgery after he was wounded before the surrender of 1942. He had saved his life. He had intentionally kept Eddie in the hospital longer than Eddie thought necessary. He had reunited with Eddie in Camp Cabanatuan and had been with him ever since. They were true friends, and Jack did his best to watch out for Eddie. When they arrived at Moji, the Japanese had taken all the doctors aside and advised them that they needed to choose the 100 sickest men. They assured Jack and the others that they would be taken to a hospital close by where they would be well taken care of. The other 450 men would be housed in the area.

When the doctors came away from their pow-wow with the Japanese officials, Eddie saw Jack look around the room to find him. They made eye contact and Jack made his way through the crowd. He told Eddie the Japs had asked for the most ill prisoners. They would only take 100 and Jack had given them Eddie's name. Eddie had come out of the Hell ships in better shape than men twenty years his junior. Jack felt that if Eddie were in a hospital, he would get better food and care. He truly felt it wasn't going to be that long before the cavalry came to save them all. He wanted what was best for Eddie and this was, in his best professional opinion, the right thing to do. Eddie trusted Jack and thanked him for his concern and subsequent decision. Eddie reminded Jack of their pact and both men shook hands once more. Jack never saw Eddie again.

450 prisoners were then divided into three groups. Each group was being sent to a different location, but all were close by. Eddie had been assigned to Camp Fukuoka #3.

52

Eddie was happy to see that his old friend Colonel "Zero" Wilson would be with him at Fukuoka #3. He was distraught when he thought about the loss of all the Lt. Colonels. There were 35 in all when they had started their journey. There were now just seven remaining, including Eddie and Wilson. Three were in their group here and were gravely ill. Wilson was senior officer and had graduated from West Point in 1924, one year before Eddie. He and Eddie would become inseparable in the coming days and weeks. With only one blanket for every two men, they would share each other's warmth in order to survive.

The conditions at Fukuoka #3 were deplorable. The hospital that neighbored the barracks was so appalling that no one but officers were allowed access unless they were sick. Eddie wasn't aware of the other camp's conditions, but if they were anything like this sewer, he feared few would survive. All the men were in agreement that someone, anyone, had to make it out of this squalor so the world would know what had happened to them—all of it. The Nips had to be held accountable.

When they were assigned to their barracks, the group of 100 was small enough for Eddie to take a true assessment of everyone's health. It was pathetic. There were men who literally had to be cared for like babies, 24 hours a day. Eddie stepped up to the challenge immediately and cared for as many as he could handle. Feeding and cleaning grown men when one was only a shadow of themselves was something Eddie could do to keep his focus. No one was surprised with Eddie's attitude or work ethic. This was who he was—a decent human being who cared for those less fortunate than himself. And he was a senior grade officer. What was rare was the fact that he did it with a smile on his face and never gave up on his optimism.

Little did the men know, but the American B-29 Super-Fortresses were raining death down on the Japanese cities and industrial hubs. Phosphorous bombs had reduced Tokyo, Kyoto, Osaka, and other major metropolises, to smoldering rubble. Hundreds of thousands had been consumed in the fire storms. Wave after wave of all-weather bombers revisited their nightly runs over the Japanese heartland and its civilian population. The intensity of the fires sucked in so much air from their surrounding districts that it created a blast furnace effect, impossible to extinguish with the primitive firefighting equipment brandished against it. The wood and paper houses literally exploded from their proximity to the inferno. For Japan, it was the end of the world. And if it was the end of the world, then their last breath and hope would lie with the 7,000 volunteers to fly suicide missions into the approaching American flotilla. Not only would this sacrifice bring honor, pilots would be advanced two grades, given a hero's funeral while his soul would be enshrined in the Yasukuni Temple of the Warriors in Chiyoda.

The end of the world brought the rebirth of the Kamikaze—the Divine Wind, which centuries earlier had defeated the impending naval assault from the Mongul invading force, and now would challenge the very nerve and focus of the American navy. Such was the mentality of the Japanese—to sacrifice for the life of their nation, their Emperor Hirohito, and to bring honor to themselves and their family. Conversely, the American prisoners had brought shame down on themselves. They deserved nothing, and they were dying in droves now due to this traditional martial philosophy. Yet, surely some must survive. Someone must provide witness to this inhumanity. Eddie and the few remaining survivors would live to see this happen. There was no death wish in these brave Americans, they would endure to their last breath.

53

Eddie passed February tending to the sick and staying close to the little stove in their barracks, reminiscing with the other officers. They would spend hours talking about the days before the war. They talked of their liberation. They tried to avoid the here and now... rather they preferred to remember special meals they'd eaten or restaurants they'd visit again when the war was over. They deliberated over food constantly. They knew their poor emaciated bodies were slowly wasting away. Eddie listened intently, hoping that all this talk about juicy steaks and creamy sauces would re-invigorate his own appetite. He had been having some trouble keeping his meals down. Rice and watery soup was the only sustenance the men received at Fukuoka. It was not unusual for men's severely shrunken stomachs to revolt against the same bland diet they faced, day in and day out.

Basically, the capacity to digest food was lost. Starvation is a slow process and eventually the body begins to cannibalize itself. Eddie knew this ailment could have serious consequences but was confounded as to what could be done. He would will his food to stay down.

At the beginning of March, Eddie was making some repairs on the barracks. The frigid and icy winds of the Japanese winter were howling through a crack in the back wall, and Eddie was able to use a rock and a scrap of metal to jam up the hole. It was awkward; he smashed his left index finger. Mumbling obscenities to himself once the initial "Damn" had left his lips, he lurched back to the warmth of the stove and the company of his buddies. Within a few days, the finger became infected. Zero guided Eddie to the hospital. It wasn't like the place had antibiotics to cure him, but the doctors were American and he would get the best care the place had to offer. He seemed comfortable in the hospital despite the filth and death all around him. Zero checked on him every day and promised Eddie he would return to the barracks in no time. There were several enlisted men that Eddie knew well and they convalesced together under dire circumstances. The men tried to get Eddie to keep his food down, with no luck.

One evening Eddie pulled his ring out. It had been a particularly bad day. Men were dying all around him and the smell of death permeated his soul. He rubbed the ring's cold surface as if it were a Genie's bottle. He smiled to himself because Nancy had teased him about his weight when they had been moved to the Philippines.

He enjoyed food immensely, and as an officer, his physical health wasn't as important as it had been in his early career. She had pressed him to lose weight, but she would be aghast at his shrunken appearance now. In the few months here at Fukuoka, he had lost so much weight that she wouldn't recognize him when he got off the ship in Manila. He knew the promise to put some of those pounds back on lay with Nancy's tasty home cooking—in the not too distant future, as he prayed.

As he carefully replaced the ring in its hiding place in his shirt sleeve, a humming sound could be heard in the distance. The whine of a plane, probably a B-29, was getting louder as it approached the camp. The collective breath of every sick soldier stopped as the whistling bomb plummeted though the night air. The plane had dropped its deadly cargo and veered away as everyone waited for the detonation. It landed with an amazing thud, very close by. The ground failed to undulate. There was no shock wave, no debris slicing through the air. Loud, chaotic Japanese swearing could be heard outside. The goosebumps on Eddie's whole body stood at attention. He broke out in a cold sweat as he realized they'd missed death again. The bomb had failed to detonate. It was a dud, for God's sake. Everyone anticipated another bombing run, but the plane never returned. Eddie closed his eyes and said a prayer of thanks for their narrow escape.

Deep sleep came to no one that night. Every man in the room dreamed of a deadly explosion, not once but many times as they pleaded for their minds to rest. Early the next morning, their nightmares became reality when the damned Japs couldn't leave well enough alone. They intentionally exploded the warhead and blew the roof off the hospital, shrapnel penetrating the thin walls, killing several of their own in their meddling. Thus, Eddie and twenty other survivors from the hospital were transferred back to the barracks. No medical personnel were moved with them, so Zero assigned an able officer to each invalid. Eddie received the undying care of Major Gus Francis. Gus was from Salt Lake City, Utah and even though he was coughing and ill himself, he was devoted to Eddie and gave him the attention he needed to carry on. The two men had known each other throughout the ordeal and, as Gus was younger, Eddie had tried to be a father figure to him. Eddie's infection had slowed, but he was weak from unintentional starvation and nothing was likely to change. It would only get worse. Gus knew that if the army knights didn't arrive soon, they would find his friend dead.

54

At the end of March, Eddie contracted dysentery. His body had no defenses left to fight it. In early April, he was unable to leave his straw mat in the barracks. He had no strength; he was emaciated, a mere contorted shell of a man. Gus couldn't keep him hydrated. Absolutely nothing stayed down. Starvation had finally won out. The army knights would not reach Eddie in time.

On his last evening, Eddie murmured constantly about Nancy and Johnny. He haltingly tore at his shirt sleeve and freed the ring. He shook terribly, but once centered, the ring slipped easily on his skeletal left ring finger. Eddie recalled the night Johnny had been born and how brave Nancy had been. Eddie loved the part about sitting in the room in the dark while Nancy slept. He had seen a light all night long. In the morning, he'd realized it was the Statue of Liberty. It was like a special sign for their life together and the sacrifices they would both have to make for their country. Gus listened, then wrapped Eddie's ring back into his sleeve after all his stories. Before he fell asleep he told Gus, his voice now in a troubled, raspy whisper, "We all must go and I'm sinking fast. Please tell my darling wife that I'm with her and that she is to take very good care of the boy." Those were Eddie's last words. He closed his eyes and perhaps dropped off to sleep sometime around 2:00 am in the morning on April 9, 1945, exactly three years to the day of the American surrender of Bataan.

When Gus checked on Eddie several hours later, the body had already been moved. Later that morning, a service was held in Eddie's honor. Gus, Zero, and the remaining men who could still stand were in attendance. It was a simple memorial. Every man chose to speak a few words. To a man, each spoke of Eddie's relentless optimism and compassion for his fellow soldiers. No one cried, not because they didn't want to but because their exhaustion and acceptance of the inevitable wouldn't allow it. Eddie's body was removed to the crematorium and his ashes were brought back to the camp. Here they remained until they were returned to Manila after the Japanese surrender.

Nancy received a letter, dated September 16, 1945, from a dear friend whose husband was close to Eddie. The letter began, "Keep me posted, and I'll do the same. My heart is breaking within me as I write you this letter..." The War Department death notification telegram didn't arrive until November 16, 1945. Eddie had been dead for over seven months.

Camp Cabanatuan was liberated on January 30, 1945. On March 8, its 272 freed prisoners arrived in San Francisco. On September 2, 1945, the Japanese surrendered.

With his still-grieving mother by his side, Johnny accepted each of his father's medals posthumously. Five times he stood at attention, now seven years old and the man of the family. The Purple Heart for Eddie's wounds on Bataan, the Silver Star for Gallantry in Action on Bataan, the Bronze Star for meritorious achievement on Bataan, and two Oak Leaf Clusters for meritorious service as Provost Marshal and his work in the underground in Camp Cabanatuan now graced his small but proud chest. One of the Bronze Medal Oak Leaf Clusters was presented by Colonel Harold K. Johnson, who had been a Prisoner of War with Eddie.

Johnny had no memory of his father, but his mother's consistent and vital recounting of Eddie's noble endeavors and courageous deeds would solidify his hero status in Johnny's heart and mind forever. Each medal weighed very little, yet Johnny felt their heaviness long after they had been removed and put in a velvet box for safe keeping. As an only child, Johnny knew at a very young age the significance of a father serving his country. He would be his father's son, of that he was certain.

Eddie's ashes were moved to Manila where they remained in a crypt at the United States Military cemetery until they could make the trip home. In the spring of 1948, they were exhumed and returned to Nancy in Leavenworth, Kansas. Because he was awarded the Silver Star for his work in the underground, Eddie could have been interred at Arlington National Cemetery in Washington, D.C., but Nancy chose to have him close by.

Lt. Colonel Edward Mack was laid to rest at Ft. Leavenworth National Cemetery on a late Friday afternoon in February of 1949. Several of Eddie's classmates from West Point were studying at Ft. Leavenworth's Command and General Staff College at the time and acted as pall bearers. Members of the Mack family traveled from Pennsylvania to be at the graveside. Johnny, remembered this solemn event as vividly many years later as he did the day it happened. It was a tragic end to a hero's short but eventful life—born in Pennsylvania, in combat and imprisoned in the Philippines, killed in Japan, and buried in Kansas.

EPILOGUE

The ring was gold and cold. The garnet stone had been chipped, a section gone, missing. Crafted by Tiffany and Company, its design was covered with symbols and mottos. West Point and the graduation date of 1925 were carved prominently around the stone. Inside, where it rode close to a man's finger, there had once been a name. Now only scratches remained because the name was purposefully removed to hide its real owner.

The ring had been in a dark place for a long, long time. It wasn't alone though. It had a twin of sorts. The other was scratched, but the defiler had been sloppy and six letters were still legible. The graduation date was 1934. Both rings were in a leather drawstring bag wrapped in tissue and snuggled in a corner of the safety deposit box. Other items were strewn about, including old worn Filipino pesos, a hand-made spoon and bowl, and hundreds of fragments of tin can labels, newsprint, and assorted match flap covers. Each was covered with tiny writing, so small they were hard to read, so little space between the letters and words.

But it is the 1925 ring that draws our interest. Not its financial worth as a piece of 1920's gold on the Antique Road Show. No, it is in its intrinsic value to the family of the true American hero that wore it. This is its genuine importance.

When next the ring sees the light of day, it is 2006. The owner of the safety deposit box would die an old man in Los Angeles, and the keys to the box would be handed over to his nephew. The nephew was unaware that his uncle was a civilian WWII POW that survived imprisonment at the Japanese Camp Fukuoka #3. He was also not sure why his uncle would have two West Point graduate rings in his box. It would take the assistance of his Eagle Scout son, who remembered his Scoutmaster was a West Pointer, to help them find the ring's owner.

Months pass before Edward Clement Mack's ring made its way home. With the help of modern technology, in the form of a blog called the *Philippine Scouts Heritage Society,* the West Point Ring Recovery program, and a West Point archivist who still had the 1925 class ring order records, the ring's owner would be identified. Based on his graduation date, his imprisonment at Camp Fukuoka #3 and his ring size, Edward Mack's ten and a half would fly overnight express into the hands of his son, Colonel John Mack.

The ring is still gold, but it is no longer cold. It warms quickly in John's hands; the only tangible piece of his father that he had ever seen, touched, or remembered.

What Happened to Them After

Lorenza or Larry Amusategui (Screwball) survived the war and, like Naomi, contacted Nancy about wartime activities in the underground. She was a witness at the Japanese War Crimes Trials and like many in the Miss U group was discouraged that the acknowledgement and respect she and particularly her dead husband were deserving of was not initially forthcoming. She married an American, Captain Edward O'Malley in 1946 which would give her a new life in the United States. In 1948, she was awarded the Medal of Freedom, and her deceased husband Ramon was given the Medal of Freedom with a Gold Palm, the highest civilian honor. A bill was passed in the U.S. Congress which allowed her two sons to come to America, and her new husband adopted them both. The family settled in the one place that Ramon was willing to give his life for.

Ramon Amusategui (Sparkplug) died before the war ended, at Fort Santiago at the hands of the Japanese. His significance in the underground can never be overstated. He was a resistance fighter with the Philippine guerrillas and his bravery and leadership enabled Utinsky's network to not only function, but endure. Ramon and his wife Lorenza were instrumental in the movement of goods and money to aid the prisoners at Camp Cabanatuan, and it was Ramon's genius that made it happen. His dream was to survive the war and take his family to live in the United States.

Naomi Flores (Looter) survived the war and her correspondence with Nancy Mack about her work with Eddie and the underground was lengthy and regular, especially for the first four years right after the war. She wrote to Nancy about Eddie keeping death records at Camp Cabanatuan and his original map of the camp that he eventually had her turn over to a reliable Filipino guerrilla. Important information was passed between Eddie and Ramon Amusategui, also a high-ranking member of the Filipino guerrillas, about Japanese movements in the north of the Philippines. This secret and deadly information was strategic in the waning months of the war. Naomi made statements for the War Crimes investigations in 1946 of Japanese atrocities in the Philippines, witnessed during the war. As a member of the Fort Santiago Prisoner's Association (where she was imprisoned for sheltering American POWs), she worked tirelessly at getting recognition for the Filipinos who engaged in wartime activities against the Japanese. In 1948, Naomi was finally recognized with the Medal of Freedom. Two months after the award, she left Manila to come to America. She was able to meet with some of the surviving POWs she had assisted, including Jack Schwartz. She married John Jackson, an American who had been involved in the War Crimes Trials in the Philippines. They had a daughter who, 40 years later, as a student officer at the Ft. Leavenworth Command and General Staff College, was able to meet Nancy Mack.

John Hassig (brother of Nancy Mack) was stationed in the Philippines at the end of the war and was asked by his sister to make contact with as many of Eddie's surviving underground ring as he could find. He was able to meet Naomi Flores, Lorenza (Larry) Amusategui, Fred Threatt, and Horacio Manalato and his family. He was also able to type up the letters written by Eddie to Naomi and the few surviving letters from Eddie to Lorenza and Ramon Amusategui. All were used in this book. Finally, he visited the Personal Claims Office in Manila to inquire about Eddie's diary, but none was ever found. However, not one person in the office had to look up Eddie's name. They all knew him and his reputation and the work he had done for not only his country but theirs.

Harold K. Johnson ended the war in a POW camp in Inchon, Korea and was liberated on September 7, 1945. After the war, he first attended the U.S. Army Command and General Staff College in Ft. Leavenworth, Kansas, followed by the Armed Forces Staff College in Norfolk, Virginia, graduating in 1949. In 1950, when the North Koreans invaded South Korea, he was put in command of a provisional infantry battalion. When the battalion reached Korea, Johnson's leadership during the Chinese invasion in the fall earned him the Distinguished Service Cross, our nation's second highest award for heroism. He later was the commandant of the Command and General Staff College at Ft. Leavenworth. During the Vietnam War, he would become the Army Chief of Staff. He died in 1983 at the age of 71.

(Note from the publisher... As a young lieutenant, I had breakfast with GEN Harold K. Johnson in Vietnam on Christmas morning, 1966. I had no idea he had been a POW in WWII, it was just a great honor to have breakfast with the Chief of Staff of the Army. The impression I remember was he was a caring and thoughtful man who cared about what we young officers having breakfast with him had to say).

John Hassig Mack attended West Point and graduated in 1961. Like his father, he was in the infantry and served as an advisor in Vietnam in 1963 and 1964. He was awarded the Bronze Star and the Combat Infantryman's Badge. He went back to Vietnam as a company commander in 1966, with the 199th Light Infantry Brigade. During his second tour in Vietnam, he was awarded the Silver Star*, a second Bronze Star with the V for valor device, and the Army Commendation Medal. He resigned from the active Army in 1969 as a major and joined the Army Reserves. He subsequently attended the Army Command and General Staff College, as well as the Army War College. He retired from the Army Reserves in 1991 as a colonel and was awarded the Meritorious Service Medal. In civilian schooling, he received a JD from Kansas University in 1971 and an LLM from George Washington University in 1972. He is retired and lives in Westlake, Ohio, but remains active in West Point Admissions.

*It merits mentioning that there are very few examples in the history of the United States and certainly West Point where both a father and son have been awarded the Silver Star in two different wars.

Nancy Hassig Mack was active during the war in the Red Cross and was head of the POW section. She worked vigorously to get Eddie's counterparts in the underground whatever help and assistance they needed after the war. She was adamant that they get the recognition they deserved for their heroics and sacrifices made for Eddie and the other prisoners in the camps. She performed tirelessly to this end. Her love of teaching never died and eventually she became principal at two different middle schools at Ft. Leavenworth, Kansas. She never remarried but remained active in community and military affairs throughout the rest of her life. She died in 1992, at the age of 84.

Horacio Manaloto (Mutt) and his family survived the war and communicated with Nancy after meeting her brother John Hassig in the Philippines at the end of the war. He told Nancy he never spoke with Eddie because their jobs in the underground were different and he was fearful of being caught by the guards. "As I sit writing this I can still remember the face of Col. Mack near the prison commissary when I made my deliveries. Although we had no exchange of verbal words in the camp for fear of consequences, our eyes spoke a lot. His letters to the group he was working with were all full of appreciation and encouragement for each individual." Manaloto and his family gave everything they owned to the underground cause and had to depend on friends for their survival after the war. In 1948, he also received the Medal of Honor with a Gold Palm which was presented at Fort McKinley in the Philippines. He wrote Nancy thirty letters about the war as well as other personal matters. When the Americans returned to the Philippines, Horacio was filled with a new optimism. His nightmares stopped and his hopes for the future of his country and his family were renewed. "We have faith that the Stars and Stripes will lead us to brighter realms of peace and prosperity."

Jack Schwartz kept his promise to Eddie and visited Nancy in Kansas City when he returned home to the States. He remained in the army and went on to become a Brigadier General in the Medical Corps. In the mid-1950s, he was the commanding officer at Walter Reed Medical Center.

Ovid O. "Zero" Wilson left Camp Fujuoka #3 on April 25, 1945 and went to Camp Hoten in Mukden, Manchuria. He survived the war and retired from the Army as a colonel in 1945. He then moved to Houston and worked for Adams and Porter, Inc., a marine insurance brokerage. He was extremely successful and retired as Chairman of the Board in 1974. He died in 1982 at 80 years old.

IMPORTANCE OF RELIABLE SOURCES

As a librarian, a big part of my job is helping students find and use reliable sources when researching. I want to talk about the importance of this skill when writing about the events of the Philippines in World War II.

When doing research, I teach my students two very important rules about primary sources: 1) time and place and 2) bias. First, the closer your source is to the time and place of the actual event, the more reliable the source. If you use my bibliography for sources, be sure to note their copyright dates. Many of the sources are memoirs because they were written decades after the events, when the men and women were much older. That doesn't mean they aren't worthy sources. The fact is that time has passed, and for most humans this means you may remember things differently. In addition, you may have read other sources whose stories may have influenced your interpretation of what you remembered.

Understand, too, that for the POWs held captive by the Japanese, most were under intense physical and mental duress. Their focus was the survival of the day to day inhumane treatment they were seeing and receiving. Every day was the same, and thoughts of keeping a record were not high on one's agenda. Plus, if you were caught writing in a journal, the penalty could be fatal. Eddie was seen writing in a journal but it has never been found. I was dependent on the letters he wrote to his wife and to the friends that wrote to her after the war.

Second and very essential to remember, all sources have bias. There are very few primary sources written by American POWs at the time of their captivity in the Philippines. Retired Colonel John Olson was a captain during his imprisonment at Camp O'Donnell and he kept a written account of his time there. Unbelievably, he was able to keep it hidden, and it survived the war. Written with a pencil in a Bureau of Education Students Note Book, it acts as an official record of Camp O'Donnell from April 11—July 5, 1942. Olson was the Personnel Adjutant and, as such, was the archivist for the American Group detained there. Is this a reliable source? Absolutely. For the time and place rule, it is truly real time. Is it biased? Absolutely. Remember, this is one perspective—that of Colonel Olson. When you do research, do you want multiple perspectives? Absolutely.

Unfortunately, we don't have written records from the Japanese officers and guards from this time-period. What thoughts and records we do have of their actions can be gleaned from a few of the soldier's testimonies from the War Crimes Trials that happened after the war. We also can make inferences about Japanese treatment of the American and Filipino soldiers from the Bushido ideology that was practiced by most of the Japanese military.

Both of these rules, used by all good historians, can still lead you to the truth. How you say? By using multiple sources. How many you say? As many as you can find and peruse. Somewhere in your plethora of sources, you will find what really happened. As historians, this is all we can surely hope for.

BIBLIOGRAPHY

Alley, Lisa. "The Last Army Radio Station in the Philippines." *Corregidor Then and Now: Under Siege.* Web. 2011. Accessed 2018. http://corregidor.org/chs_signals/sigs.htm.

Ashton, Captain Paul. *Bataan Diary.* Self-published. 1984.

Bilibid Prison. Wars' Voices: Are You Listening? War Voices. Web. Jul 12, 2014. Accessed 2017. http://www.warsvoices.org/location/bilibid-prison/.Boyt, Gene Lt. *Bataan: a Survivor's Story.* Norman, Oklahoma, University of Oklahoma Press, 2004.

Flores, Naomi. Naomi Flores to Nancy Mack. Letter. October 11, 1945.

Flores, Naomi. Naomi Flores to Nancy Mack. Letter. November 16, 1945.

Flores, Naomi. Naomi Flores to Nancy Mack. Letter. January 22, 1946.

Flores, Naomi. Naomi Flores to Nancy Mack. Letter. February 19, 1946.

Flores, Naomi. Naomi Flores to Nancy Mack. Letter. March 22, 1946.

Franklin, Gus. Gus Franklin to Nancy Mack. Letter. December 17, 1945.

Janda, Lance. *The War, The Philippines (Bataan) (1942).* Web. September, 2007. http://www.pbs.org/thewar/detail_5209.htm.

Johnson, Harold K. Harold K. Johnson to Nancy Mack. Letter. November 19, 1945.

Johnson, Harold K. Harold K. Johnson to Nancy Mack. Letter. January 5, 1946.

Johnson, Harold K. Account of the Oryuku Maru Trip and on to Japan. No Date.

Lefebvre, Jim. "October 18, 1924: The Four Horsemen Arrive." *Loyal Sons: The Story of The Four Horsemen and Notre Dame Football's 1924 Champions.* University of Notre Dame Athletic Department. Web, 2017. http://125.nd.edu/moments/october-18-1924-the-four-horsemen-arrive/.

Mack, Edward. Edward Mack to Nancy Mack. Extracts from 58 letters written before December 7, 1941 after Nancy and Johnny left the Philippines.

Mack, Edward. Edward Mack to Nancy Mack. Letter. February 8, 1942.

Mack, Edward. Edward Mack to Nancy Mack. Letter. February 16, 1942.

Mack, Edward. Edward Mack to Nancy Mack. Letter. February 28, 1942.

Mack, Edward. Edward Mack to Nancy Mack. Letter. Easter Day, 1942.

Mack, Edward. Edward Mack to Naomi Flores. Letter. March 20, 1943.

Mack, Edward. Edward Mack to Naomi Flores. Letter. April 24, 1943.

Mack, Edward. Edward Mack to Naomi Flores. Letter. April 30, 1943.

Mack, Edward. Edward Mack to Naomi Flores. Letter. May 3, 1943.

Mack, Edward. Edward Mack to Naomi Flores. Letter. May 23, 1943.

Mack, Edward. Edward Mack to Naomi Flores. Letter. May 25, 1943.

Mack, Edward. Edward Mack to Naomi Flores. Letter. May 26, 1943.

Mack, Edward. Edward Mack to Naomi Flores. Letter. Undated. Friday. 1943.

Mack, Edward. Edward Mack to Naomi Flores. Letter. June 5, 1943.

Mack, Edward. Edward Mack to Naomi Flores. Letter. June 16, 1943.

Mack, Edward. Edward Mack to Naomi Flores. Letter. June 20, 1943.

Mack, Edward. Edward Mack to Naomi Flores. Letter. Undated. Friday, 1943.

Mack, Edward. Edward Mack to Naomi Flores. Letter. July 18, 1943.

Mack, Edward. Edward Mack to Naomi Flores. Letter. Undated. Monday, 1943.

Mack, Edward. Edward Mack to Ramon "Sparkie" Amusategui. Letter. August 17, 1943.

Mack, Edward. Edward Mack to Ramon "Sparkplug" Amusategui. Letter. August 30, 1943.

Mack, Edward. Edward Mack to Ramon "Sparkie" Amusategui. Letter. September 15, 1943.

Mack, Edward. Edward Mack to Ramon "Sparkie" Amusategui. Letter. September 24, 1943.

Mack, Edward. Edward Mack to Ramon "S-plug" Amusategui. Letter. February 2, 1944.

Mack, Edward. Edward Mack to Lorenza "Screwball" Amusategui. Letter. August 31, 1944.

Mack, Edward. Edward Mack to Lorenza "Screwball" Amusategui. Letter. September 3, 1944.

Manaloto, Horacio. Horacio Manaloto to Nancy Mack. Letter. December 6, 1945.

Manaloto, Horacio. Horacio Manaloto to Nancy Mack. Letter. December 18, 1945.

Manaloto, Horacio. Horacio Manaloto to Nancy Mack. Letter. December 29, 1945.

Manaloto, Horacio. Horacio Manaloto to Nancy Mack. Letter. September 24, 1946

Norman, Michael and Elizabeth M. Norman. *Tears in the Darkness: the Story of the Bataan Death March and Its Aftermath.* New York: Picador, 2010.

Olson, John E. *O'Donnell: Andersonville of the Pacific; Extermination Camp of American Hostages in the Philippines.* Self-published. 1985.

"The Oryoku Maru Story." *The Oryoku Maru Online.* 2001. Web. Accessed 2016. http://www.oryoku-maruonline.org/oryoku_maru_storyp4.html.

Pilet, Betty. Betty Pilet to Nancy Mack. Letter. September 16, 1945.

Sides, Hampton. *Ghost Soldiers: the Epic Account of World War II's Greatest Rescue Mission.* New York: Anchor, 2002.

Sitter, Lt. Colonel Stephen. Lt. Colonel Stephen Sitter to Nancy Mack. Letter. March 21, 1945.

Sloan, Bill, "Corregidor: the Last Battle in the Fall of the Philippines." *History Net.* Web. April 23, 2012. http://www.historynet.com/corregidor-the-last-battle-in-the-fall-of-the-philippines.htm. Accessed 2018.

Spector, Ronald H. *Eagle Against the Sun.* New York: Vintage, 1985.

Stamatov, Suzanne. "Cabanatuan Prisoner of War Camp—1942." *New Mexico History.org.* Web.

Accessed 2017. http://newmexicohistory.org/people/cabanatuan-prisoner-of-war-camp-1942.

Surviving Bataan and Beyond: Colonel Irvin Alexander's Odyssey as a Japanese Prisoner of War. Mechanicsburg, Pennsylvania: Stackpole Books, 1999.

MacArthur, Brian. *Surviving the Sword: Prisoners of the Japanese in the Far East, 1942-1945.* New York: Random House, 2005.

Talbot, Albert D. Albert D. Talbot to Nancy Mack. Letter. May 2, 1945.

"The Telescope That Was to Large." *Tophotshots.* September 10, 2016. Web. Accessed 2017. http://tophotshots.org/the-telescope-which-was-too-large/.

Tenney, Lester. *My Hitch in Hell.* Lincoln, Nebraska: Potomac Books, 2007.

Thompson, Jan. *The Tragedy of Bataan.* Film. Carbondale, Illinois: WSIU Public Broadcasting, Southern Illinois University at Carbondale. 2011.

Utinsky, Margaret. *Miss U.* San Antonio: Naylor Company, 1948.

War Department, Major General Edward F. Witsell. *War Citations Correspondence for Silver Star and Bronze Star.* Sent June 27, 1946.

War Department, Major General Edward F. Witsell. *War Citations Correspondence for Bronze Star Medal with Oak Leaf Cluster.* Sent November 13, 1946.

War Department, Major General Edward F. Witsell.

War Citations Correspondence for Bronze Star Medal with 2nd Oak Leaf Cluster. Sent March 3, 1948.

Whitman, John W. *Bataan: Our Last Ditch: the Bataan Campaign, 1942.* New York: Hippocrene Books, 1990.

Wilson, Colonel "Zero." Colonel Zero Wilson to Nancy Mack, Letter. December 5, 1945.

Acknowledgements

The most important person I need to thank is no longer with us. This book would not exist without Nancy Hassig Mack's love and loyalty to her husband and his legacy. She saved every photo, letter, telegram, document, and award that connected him to her. Their son, John Hassig Mack, organized all of the sources after her death and shared them with the West Point archives and eventually with me.

Finally, I am so fortunate to have a husband that is a historian like myself, but also a grammar freak, unlike myself. He taught International Baccalaureate History for 30 years and taught his students how to write while they learned about the history of the Americas and the twentieth century. His expertise is always invaluable to me. Thank you, Robbie.

About the Author

Ronda Hassig is a national board-certified library media specialist at Harmony Middle School and a Kansas Master Teacher. She is a fifth generation Kansan. Born in Lawrence, the site of Quantrill's Raid, she has always loved history. Her first book, The "Abduction of Jacob Rote," published in 2012, tells the story of a real boy who led Quantrill and his men to Lawrence the fateful morning of August 21, 1863. Her mother's side of the family came to Lawrence in November of 1863, just three months after the massacre. She is married to a retired history teacher and together, they have traveled the world. She loves to read, write and walk her three feral dogs. Whenever possible, you can find all five of them at their home away from home, which sits near the Oregon Trail.

CPSIA information can be obtained
at www.ICGtesting.com
Printed in the USA
FFOW02n0803300418
46390906-48130FF